MW00652189

About Moss.

Moss is a literary journal of the Pacific Northwest. Founded in 2014, *Moss* is dedicated to exploring the intersection of place and creative expression while exposing the region's outstanding writers to a broad audience of readers, critics, and publishers.

Moss.

Volume Four.

M. A publication of Moss.
http://mosslit.com

Twitter: @mosslitmag
Facebook: facebook.com/mosslit
mosslit@gmail.com

Defend abortion.

Printing by Bookmobile Printing Services
ISBN: 978-0-9969379-3-1

Contents.

Poetry

If we build accountability in our own social circles, in our own artistic endeavors, in our own creative life, in our own communities, then that's what actually opens up the possibility for any kind of honest connection.

Mattila Bernstein Sycamore

Who Chooses

Tara Atkinson

After my father died, I waited for his ghost. I waited for him in the church that held his body and in my uncle's house in Indiana where we stayed until the funeral was over. One night a powerful thunderstorm woke me, loud and bright. It reminded me of what summer is in the Midwest, and that I don't live there anymore. When I returned to Seattle, I continued to wait. He did not show up in my dreams. He did not appear in any of my doorways. His face did not reflect up out of the coffee mugs I took from his house.

One night the motion-activated light in my closet flipped on of its own accord, in the middle of the night. It was a very blue light, the same blue light as always. I was certain this was my father and I was frightened. I asked my husband to get out of bed and turn it off, and when he did, I knew my dad was not the light in the closet. He didn't show up for Halloween. He didn't show up for Christmas. Then I was out of ghost holidays.

I wondered if my father was able to appear to me and was, maybe, just choosing not to. If he were truly at the feet of God, for example, would he really want to check in on his daughter always slumped over a computer? In life, my father rarely did things he didn't want to do. He didn't go on our vacations to amusement parks or the church family camp. He didn't see Disney princess movies in theaters. He didn't play Mall Madness on Christmas morning. Why start dropping in now that he'd transcended life?

Sometime after my mother divorced him he left town without saying goodbye and we didn't hear from him for months. When he did call again he had remarried. I was 16. I recognized him for the first time in an adult way, as a person like I was a person, full of wanting for a different life, and I knew for the first time that all the grappling for love and acceptance I felt then wouldn't end with adulthood or parenthood.

I didn't dream about him until nine months after his death. In one dream, he toppled over onto some grass. I rushed to his side but he disappeared. On the ground, I found a brown laurel leaf I thought his hand might have turned into and I grabbed it, but right away I knew the leaf wasn't my dad after all. I went running down a path calling for him, calling "Dad." He called back to me, "Are you ok?" I found him sitting up on a cliff, looking happy. I got the impression he was there with other people, having fun. Then he disappeared again, as if following a party. He didn't wait for my response. I wanted to follow him but I couldn't find a way to climb the cliff. He was gone.

In the other dream, I was sitting on the couch beside my mom in the house I grew up in and he walked into the house, past the couch and into another room, without saying anything. My mom saw my reaction and said, "Did you see your dad?" with the same tone she used after their divorce on the very rare occasions when she'd ask if I'd heard from him lately. She was crocheting something and didn't look up.

He had wanted to be cremated, because it was more affordable, and when my uncle and my sister called me with the funeral director, I said "Ok, yes, let's do that", but I hadn't seen my father in a year and half, so thirty seconds later I said, "No, I want to see him," so he was not cremated after all. Seeing the body, they told me, would bring closure.

When I first saw his body, prepared for burial, my sister and I were sitting in the sanctuary of the church waiting for him to arrive, even though we didn't need to be there. We sat on the pews in that calm and heavy room while the bright summer light diffused through the stained-glass windows and over the green carpet and wooden pews, right there in the front row, staring at the place at the front of that room where the casket would soon be. The funeral director looked uncomfortable that we were there, and I tried to talk to my sister to make it obvious to him that I wasn't there to make sure he did a good job. I was there because it was impossible to do anything but wait in a sanctuary to see my father.

His face had been made to look a little fuller, as it looks in the photograph we selected to run with his obituary, he was wearing a suit, and he looked dead. That's what I said to my sister: "He looks dead". He looked to me more dead than any of the other dead people I'd seen at funerals. It was obvious at a glance that his body was a body and he was no longer in it. Not only was his face just a signifier for the person I knew but that's what it had always been, because here was his face, and he was not in it. And yet I still thought of the body as him. The sight of his face filled me with pity that I wasn't expecting, like you might feel when seeing pictures of starving children. I told him I was so, so sorry this had happened to him. I felt terrible that we couldn't do anything more for him than put him in a suit and put him in a box and bury him.

A few weeks after the funeral, I browsed cards in a bookstore. Along with the cards featuring flowers, witticisms, and romantic sentiments, there were a few featuring smiling skeletons. They were the usual depictions of smiling skeletons, like many I'd seen before, but now I could not comprehend them at all. For months after his death I thought about the decomposition of my father's body, because I still worried about that body he wasn't in. When winter arrived and it snowed I felt bad that the ground around him was cold. I remembered a Facebook app showing the growth of a fetus and imagined one that would tell me how far along my father's body was, as if one day, at the end of the process, he would be gone. But of course, he will never be gone. His bones will be there, and his coffin.

There is a video on the internet of a Barney parade balloon being ripped open by strong winds. The balloon handlers try so hard to keep Barney from blowing away. They lie on the ground with two other people holding them down to keep the ropes from being ripped from their hands. Then a great gash opens in Barney's belly. Inside he is pure white and empty. His expression doesn't change. He keeps smiling and waving as his opened abdomen ripples through the parade.

I remembered this video after I saw my father in his coffin. A friend had sent the video to me years before, for no particular reason, just because it was a morbidly fascinating image, and we laughed at it at the time. This friend's mother had cancer, but she survived, and his father is alive and healthy, his grandmother, too, all living. He can still laugh at that image. He is not in the club.

Two days after my father died, my best friend's father died. He texted me to apologize for not picking up when I tried to call him, because his father had just died. I had entered a new phase of life. I thought to myself, 'Now everyone's dads will start dying,' the same way you might say after the first of your friends get married, 'Now everyone is going to get married.' And they did. All year dads died.

I saw people with dead fathers everywhere. One day I was running through Pike Place market with a coworker looking for a gift for my boss's birthday. In a fudge shop a man was sitting at a table crying silently, while a woman beside him patted his back. They were tourists on vacation who had stopped into a candy store to browse sweets. The man had received some bad news and the woman, likely his partner, was not affected by the news; you could tell from her face and her sympathetic patting. This large man with a cut-off tank top and a mustache like Hulk Hogan's in a busy fudge shop for tourists, sitting and weeping silently on a little round café table: I looked past him. When we were out of the shop, my coworker said to me, "I don't think that man was feeling very well", and I shrugged.

Another day I was riding the bus home from work, when a man announced his father's death. When he boarded the bus, he loudly tried to shake hands with the man seated behind me, who brushed him off. So he changed seats and struck up a conversation with some young women. He said, "I have a good job, a good girl, but no ambition." The group discussed the nature of ambition. Then he said, "My dad died two weeks ago". "I'm sorry," the women said. The loud man said, "It's fine, we weren't close." Then he and the girls started making fun of my jacket, a purple windbreaker.

Whenever I scrolled through Facebook and saw another person with a dead dad, I said nothing to them. I scrolled past, looking for parties and funny videos, but what found me was a video of pelican very suddenly capturing a pigeon in its mouth. The pigeon is just pecking away with other pigeons and seagulls on some mowed lawn when the pelican snatches the pigeon up, who knows why. The other birds do not even seem alarmed, keep pecking away, as the pigeon thrashes inside the pelican's baggy throat sack. Feathers fly from the pelican's mouth. The pigeon keeps thrashing. The video stops before the pigeon either escapes or goes still.

He had a heart attack after a knee surgery. He wanted to be able to walk my sister down the aisle. He died weeks before the wedding. He was sixty. One of the last conversations I had with him was about buying him a new suit. He couldn't fit into the one he owned anymore and he couldn't buy a new one. My sister and I planned to buy it for him as a gift. I made a joke, to a friend, that I would rather buy him a suit for the wedding than for his funeral. So when I first saw him in his coffin, I told his corpse, "We got you into your old suit after all". I told him he looked handsome.

He did not have very many things when he died. He had a hard time getting around, a hard time getting work. In his cupboards, there were just a few canned vegetables and a box of instant mashed potatoes. The only checks he'd written were for rent and pizza. In his wallet, he had ten dollars and a gift card to Outback Steakhouse. The only thing he had a lot of were shoes, custom shoes paid for by his insurance, one shoe built taller than its pair to accommodate his uneven legs. In his small closet in his small apartment, two dozen shoes like new. We could not donate them because of their uneven build; no one else could wear the shoes. I threw them in a dumpster.

He had tendency to exclaim things like "Would you look at that!" with a child's fascination. He'd say, "Oh, lookie there!" and pause a few seconds, regarding a spectacle, then appraise it with a "Wow!" or "Neat!" He only made the expensive trip to visit me in Seattle once, a year and a half before he died. I took him to the Ballard Locks to see the boats passing through. When we saw a yacht, he turned to me and said, with pure wonder, "That guy is rich!"

Seattle has these amphibious vehicle tours called Ride the Ducks that I used to see nearly every day. My dad had mentioned the Ducks to me as something he would like to do when he came to town. But when he arrived I didn't bring them up. I could imagine exactly how much he would enjoy them and I was too embarrassed to Ride the Ducks with him.

That trip was the last time I saw him alive, and after I returned home that summer, I was haunted by Ride the Ducks tours passing me, day after day, downtown. He's riding them now, a friend told me. I imagined my ghost dad Riding the Ducks instead of visiting me. The next summer the tours stopped because of a terrible accident. When I heard about the accident, I imagined my ghost dad cheerfully welcoming the people who'd died to the afterlife.

I did not want to leave his body at the cemetery, but we had to leave: we the living, into our cars; my father, the deceased, into the ground, where he would be alone. I sat there until everyone else was waiting for me, then I took a last appraisal of the flowers that would be his company and followed.

After the funeral, ladies from the church brought hams and pies for the family. They lined up with their husbands to say goodbye to my dad. They told me he was a good man, that he's with Jesus now, that we'll see him again soon. They post the same things to his Facebook wall, letting him know they miss him, asking him to say hi to Jesus for them, and so forth.

When he announced my father's death, my uncle said that my father had left the land of the dying to join the land of the living. That this is a land of the dying is obvious to me. I struggle to imagine a land of the living.

My husband reads a lot of Buddhist books, but of the wisdom he tries to share with me the only concept that's stuck is samsara: suffering. I think of samsara while I watch myself in the mirror in the morning, putting on makeup. When I first wake up, every morning, I do a quick inventory—I am in my bed, it is morning, my husband is here, my father is dead, it's time to get ready for work.

When I go downtown to my office, I pass a man with a Jesus sign. He is the only person in my daily life who talks about Jesus, the only person in my daily life in any way connected to my father and the place we're from, so I have a special attachment to the man with the Jesus sign, and if he says, "God bless you" to me, thousands of miles fold up for an instant. Then I am in the lobby with fresh flowers. Then I am in the elevator with people in suits.

I pay my bills on time, earn a salary, keep in my wallet little cards for the grocery store, the library, my health insurance. I live in a nice apartment with a door code and neighbors who have get-togethers, still married, sometimes praised by my peers, exercising daily for my health, with a hook for my keys by the door, and still I feel like a child lost in the grocery store, separated from my father, with this gnawing feeling that he is not hearing his name on the overhead speakers, that he will not find me.

When he died there were voicemails on my phone that I had not listened to. They said "Happy Valentine's Day. I'm glad you had fun in Hawaii. My blood pressure is the lowest it's been since I met your mother. Probably it was high because of her, she had my heart working so hard from the moment I met her." They said "Hey, this is your dad. Happy New Year. I hope you have a good year. I'll try to see you again this year. Love you. Miss you. I'll talk to you later."

I loved his voice. I saved his voicemails so I could play them for my friends and coworkers. They delighted in his Midwest accent.

After he died the leaves turned and fell. The grass was brown and branches bare. Then crocuses, then daffodils. Cherry trees filled the gutters with the pink confetti of their petals. The heavy pompoms of peonies bowed over, gave way to dahlias. On the anniversary of his death corpse flowers bloomed in several cities. In the city I live in they called our corpse flower a dud. In my sister's apartment, the peace lily she took from his funeral bloomed, too.

Who chooses these answers.

—◁o▷—

First Lady

Anis Gisele

My aunt does not consider herself
      young.
She does not consider herself
      thin or unlucky.

She is married to a man my mother never argues with
      because he has money.

My uncle tells people he speaks to God. He will not tell my aunt
      where their daughter came from.

He says voices from the light told him she was theirs.

      Their daughter is twelve. When she hesitates before saying her father
helps people, I can see now she will one day call his work   something else.

My uncle thinks he is God's encore,
thinks he has all the universe's teeth,

tells my aunt what to eat and when to fast.

She says she and my uncle don't have sex anymore.
It is what he wants: to keep the moon inside of him.

He yells at her.   She says it is fine.

    I nod like I believe.

For so long, she has listened to people call him *master*. She thinks he is
hers too.

Women from Manila quickly learn our size. We are only as big
    as our country,
        and our country
  is small, a bed crowded
    with soldiers,
a wound infested
    with priests.

    My aunt grew up in the time of Marcos.

Women who spoke out against him were found with

    burnt
    mouths,

  bruised
  veins,

    serrated
    flesh.

Women who spoke out against him were never found.

When my aunt was a little girl, Imelda Marcos was First Lady.

She stood by her man. All the little girls saw.

My uncle met Imelda last year.
  My brother, born and raised in America, asks me
who Marcos is. I say, *A dictator.*
  My uncle corrects me, *A visionary.*

My uncle and aunt slow-dance.

  Pause.

    The
      floor tilts.

She does not let go.

—<o>—

A Couple Walks Up the Logging Road

Ruby Hansen Murray

Mid-morning in early summer fog haloes float off whaleback ridges along the Columbia. A skein of moisture overhead promises to cool the day a little longer.

Near the river, the valley is open to thigh high grass and skunk cabbage leaves, to the nubbed arms of fir coated with moss. A fringe of lichen, the small starry hands of vine maple, swordferns, blades of grass.

We park at the juncture of roads that lead up Nelson Creek or Alger Creek and walk to the locked metal gate where Campbell Global has posted a list of rules. It's Sunday, no log trucks will pass, no hunters this time of year.

We walk a road paved with fist-sized rock to a fork and she chooses the right. Grass in the center of the path, the rocks turn to pebbles pressed into dry ground.

We can see forty miles downriver to the blue-green mound of Tongue Point and a scrape of dredge sand piled on Tennashille Island. There's the sweetness of white-flowered clover along the road. The pointed dark green of a thistle still wrapped like a pear with wispy threads.

His lean silhouette on the smaller cross ridge as he holds binoculars. He says, "There's a ship at anchor."

We watch a cargo ship's masts move above the tips of the firs along the river. Two blasts of a horn, although we can only see a fishing boat no larger than a white cap.

He wants to see a snake and a bear. Honey bees and a bumblebee nectar along the road. She wants to lose weight, to float up the hill, to walk all day.

We name the points, knobs with scraggly trees like a cowlick. Crown Point, Wickiup, Skamokawa. Power lines and a tower.

He steps over one can, rusted flat. No glinting Clamato and Bud cans.

Along the ridge, she looks down the steep incline into the lower branches of 100-foot tall Doug fir. In the great emptiness along the river, bald patches of dirt, clear-cuts.

"You know you can't have large life-less patches anymore," he says. "It's against the law."

As if we need environmentally friendly clear-cuts. On the ridge across, one tree left standing, so tall it looks like a spar. Some yards away a shorter tree. Leave trees for mitigation.

On the way back to the truck, down the rolling pebbles and ankle-turning rocks, a black lump of licorice slug.

She looks for shadows on the near ridges, but finds no elk or deer, bobcat, skunk, raccoon or possum. Tire treads dried in gray silt.

He says, "If we had taken the other road, we would have connected with the road on the next creek." He draws the road to the north in the air.

NO UNAUTHOR
VEHICLE

- The privilege of entry may be revoked at any
- WALK IN ONLY.
- NO OFF-ROAD VEHICLES.
- There is no assurance the land or roads are s

"Around that curve is where I saw the cougar."

John Hoven—with his beard curling down his chest—said, I'm sixty-four and I've seen two cougar and five bears in my life.

A chickadee flies across the road. When she hears the five note call, she repeats it, waits for the reply, while they walk down hill, the stub of her toes against her shoes.

An inch-long dragonfly. A glint of blue on gravel, a burst of jay above soft-gray-frizz. He carries the feather between his thumb and the glass of his phone.

She says, "Salmon berry."
He points and says, "Oregon grape."
A pause. "Salal."
"Aren't they the same?" He asks.
Mahonia aquifolium, she thinks, smelling the yellow stickiness of it.
"No, Oregon grape has pointed leaves."

He looks for language they can speak, for a project, for joy. She studies the sides of the road for paths the elk might have taken. She wants to bring a chair, a picnic lunch, to walk into the woods left standing, to smell the ground where the elk rested.

Off Risk Road, white windows on a shingle wall, a porch the length of the house, two chairs ready for evening. The diesel engines of ghost trucks and men shouting.

—<o>—

Be Okay, It Will Be Okay

John Englehardt

Six years before college, you are under a queen-sized mattress with your grandma and brother. A cold front has descended from the Rocky Mountains into the Plains of Arkansas, where you live in your basement-less house. Just minutes ago, you walked barefoot into the street and beheld a half-mile wide funnel cloud cutting across the landscape, the strangest gray you've ever seen, a sort of whirling, irradiated charcoal. Grandma told you to put on shoes and get under the mattress, and now she is reciting the Lord's Prayer. You are listening to hectoring gusts of wind, pictures and pill bottles smashing against the wall. Even under the mattress, you can tell when you're beneath a giant shadow. Grandma says not to grab hold of the mattress if it slips away, but when the walls heave outward and the mattress ascends, you can't help but grab after it. You go airborne and are tumbling, swapping backdrops. Earth. Sky. Earth. Sky. Earth. Sky. At some point, you see a brown trail of destruction wending across the green countryside.

Your body lands on dirt, but the wind skips and drags you across it until you hit a retaining wall, which is actually your neighbor's house that has been reduced to a slab of concrete. Your face hits it, fracturing your skull and breaking your nose, but you don't feel that yet. You stand up. It's quiet, except for a low ringing sound that howls all around you, and the sky is a floating junkyard. A Banker's chair. Chimney Bricks. 100-pound manhole. Full-bloomed poplar tree. A garage door spinning like a frisbee into the horizon. You don't know where to stand, but that's irrelevant because the wind is pushing you. Your heels dig into the ground. Sideways debris stabs into your skin like candles into a birthday cake.

When it stops, sirens blare in the distance. RVs from the dealership down the road are in ditches, shredded like paper. Amidst the ruin you find your grandmother, who at first is just a wad of disorderly gray hair, her body half-covered by a sheet of particleboard. You pull her out and dust her off, but she doesn't respond to your touch. Eventually, you scan the landscape for your brother, slowly realizing how lucky you were to find anything at all in this mosaic of rubble.

Your mom, who was shuffling cards at the casino in Alla Vista when the tornado hit, shows up in her truck, and she drives you to a medical triage outside the Dollar General where they poorly sew up the gash on your forehead and take all the debris out of your back. One thing they find is a metal pin engraved with the words MEL'S LOGGING COMPANY—IN GOD WE TRUST, which will be attached to your backpack when I meet you for the first time, many years from now.

Your mother takes you to her boyfriend's house to live, and over the course of the next year, she locks herself in the bathroom more and more. She treats you like a hole in the floor she has learned to avoid. She is harnessed to the couch with cheap rum called "El Residente," watching movies like *Home for the Holidays* in mid-July. Her boyfriend is a forklift operator who sleeps on a water bed and obsessively collects bottle caps, supposedly for some kind of "art project." He watches you sweep the kitchen like there's something inside you he's about to disinter. Then one day, he disappears, and your mom is alone in his room, yelling at a part of herself who cannot hear, surrounded by dirty clothes and cat litter ground into the carpet.

During this time, one of your teachers learns that you're stealing rolls of toilet paper from school to take home, and then CPS gets involved.

Then it's foster homes. Edges of familial units. High school vicissitudes until finally you get adoptive parents. You change your name to Rose, work at the Baskin Robbins in the mall, use your 4-H leadership experience to qualify for a poultry science scholarship at Ozarka University, a flagship state school, tucked away against one of the oldest mountain ranges in North America, where there never has been an F5 tornado, as far as you know.

When you visit, it's a land of white mansions on the edge of campus, yellow trumpets of daffodils, gigantic porch settees, and blonde girls walking in groups, all wearing the same high-waisted jean shorts. When you see how they study under dim chandeliers and cheer for the Ozarka Raccoon football team, you decide you want to join a sorority. Your adoptive parents advise against it, but you've been saving money scooping ice cream. You have enough to pay for annual dues.

Fall arrives, and you rush. You buy the right clothes. Force-smile so much that your face hurts. You line up and get honked at by every Jeep and scooter-driving male in the vicinity. And then you get into one of the most prestigious sororities, Beta Omega Kappa. The truth is, they think you are pretty—someone even says that scar on your forehead is charming, that it rips apart the conventionality of a pretty face. And you're calculating. You bury your accent, say "that would be lovely" like it's a catchphrase. You explain that you're originally from Alaska (though your only connection to that place is your biological father spent two summers there on fishing boats). You deflect unwanted attention by interrogating others. You learn to act like you're at the center of your own small universe.

So you stand there on the immaculate lawn with your sisters, two days before school starts, and they are teaching you the BOK cheer, which has a refrain that goes like this: "Be okay, it will be okay!" Amidst the high-spirited unison, you remember that all your life, you wanted to be this brand of normal—carefree, upper class, and virtuous by means of your inaccessibility—but you couldn't be. You tried so hard. You imagined this normalcy as if it were down some declivity in your heart, something you always had but could never reach. It was like growing up with an ocean outside of your bedroom window that disappeared when you looked at it. But now, on the BOK lawn, you feel like you are wading into its waters for the first time, and you are finding it is warm, and the sand is fine.

At first, you are overwhelmed by the frenetic 450-acre campus. There are tanning wipes and condoms in vending machines. Pasta bars. Students conducting Bible study in coffee shops, reading verse from iPhones, holding hands to pray while their legs squirm beneath tables. Hours-worth of coiffed hair. Lurid binge-drinking. And when you go to see your advisor in the Don Butler Center for Poultry Excellence building, you walk past an 8-foot tall bronze statue of a rooster, wearing what looks like a crown of thorns on its head. Everything is hallowed. Everyone wants to know your name.

But when classes start, you find that all your professors are burned out teaching assistants who give you worksheets, overuse PowerPoint, speak in fake-authoritarian voices, or otherwise solicit class participation like manic-depressive game show hosts. Students shop for portable hammocks and watch cooking shows on their phones during lecture. Sometimes, you feel as if you're learning what you studied in high school, just in bigger rooms with nicer computers.

One of these classes is Eddie Bishop's section of English 120. His teaching style is one of controlled outrage, directed at everything except the students sitting before him, who he attempts to "level with." Whenever his class ends, you walk out of Campbell Hall onto the cobbled road. It's late in the day, so campus no longer looks like a bad TV show. There are no boys shouting from luxury SUVs. There are no officious "Help a Raccoon" stations, no hi-fives, no slow-walking athletes, no student-ministers standing on five gallon buckets, duct tape over mouths, holding signs that say I WILL NOT BE SILENT ABOUT MY FAITH. No. It's just you in the sunset's dying lushness, the brutalist stone buildings. On these evenings,

Eddie's lectures sometimes give you an emptied-out feeling, like you are un-learning the things you thought you knew. You decide that this is what you were looking for when you came to a university.

One day, Eddie makes everyone read a short story about a girl with a wooden leg who decides to be ugly. She changes her name to Hulga, studies philosophy, wears skirts with horses on them. Eddie says she wants ugliness to create a new self. She succeeds until a Bible salesman tricks her and steals her fake leg. You read a paragraph aloud in class—the one with her stranded and one-legged in a barn—then you raise your hand and say that the ugly girl no longer clings to her ugliness, she's just sad. Eddie nods. "We have to consider," he says, now pacing past the empty first row, "that our personalities are deep wells into which the world will drop ideas, desires, even other people. So, you have to be careful. You have to know what was down there in the first place."

This is when you begin to fear the thing you made inside yourself. You spend as much time on schoolwork as you do making posters with glitter glue. You always need a date. You've been tanning, and the fair-skinned girls are starting to ask if you're "mixed with something" (i.e. Mexican, though they often guess Italian). At parties, older boys hand you drinks they made in other rooms. They take you out onto sleeping porches and tell you not to be so stingy with your body. It all feels like the story about the ugly girl, except reversed.

All of this does not completely metastasize until a representative from Slendertone Fitness comes to the sorority. She has bins filled with bands that fit around your stomach and legs, sending shocks to your muscles to tone them. All the sisters who are infinitesimally "overweight" are named, encouraged to buy said equipment, and they do. You're not one of the "fat" ones, but after this encounter, you feel that your routine of long jogs and avoiding Chicken Finger Fridays wasn't for yourself after all, but was actually in preparation for this moment. Nowadays, even the things you thought you did for yourself were not. They were for the normal person you were creating, who is now metamorphosing within you.

Amidst all this, you think increasingly about your family. Some memories emerge so clearly from those hardscrabble days that you experience them again, as if for the first time. At twelve years old, you are with your mother at the mall, and you are watching her talk to the boy selling phones at the Verizon kiosk. Your mother asks for the cheapest one, fumbling with her welfare card, and the tattooed, multi-earringed boy grabs a clamshell phone from the case, price-matches it to another store, and gives it to your mother for free. On the way home, you consider the dirty summer-dress your mother is wearing—the blue one swimming with cartoon fishes—and your own decaying shoes and barely-healed forehead, and you decide you look like someone who needs to be given things, and that you don't want to be.

You spend so much time evaluating boys the same age your brother would be that you become a sort of connoisseur. Their posture, hair-thickness, the shoulder from which their backpack hangs. One afternoon, you see a skinny, dark-haired boy in the park, eating a torta from La Super Quesadilla, his green flannel tucked into jeans, how the bright sun makes the grass around him look blanched and lost. Is that him, staring ambiguously past the swings in your direction?

That night, you lie awake in your dorm with your laptop, studying your old neighborhood with Google Street View, and you find that the cameras haven't been back since the tornado hit. You click past your grandmother's house, the waist-high chain link fence before the unkempt grass, sagging gutters, and chewed up screen door. You click on the arrows until you're down at the supermercado you used to walk to with your brother, and when you see two figures with garbled faces waiting at a crosswalk, sodas in hand, you cry so hard you can feel it deep in your jaw.

Lately, you've been feeling best when working on your term paper for Eddie's class. You've decided to write about the ugly girl, about the artificial things we lean on, like beauty and religion. You read Malebranche, study nihilism, meet with Eddie one-on-one in places like Starbucks and Slim Chickens because he doesn't like his office. He says things like "good stories have no meaning" and "you have to consider education as artifice." It all feels a little absurd, but at least it's an absurdity you're free to imitate.

When you hand in the paper on the last day of class, all you can think about is getting it back. You will sit beside Eddie at a small coffee table, wearing a dress that you hope makes you look older, all your papers neatly aligned in a binder. At some point, his admiration will overflow, and he'll say something off-kilter, something like "you have no idea who you are," but he will say it like a compliment. He will use words like incomparable, exacting, perigee. You will walk with him across the anodyne campus and into the afterlife of the person you once were.

This is what happens instead. A student walks into the library during finals week with a modified Chinese-type SKS assault rifle, then opens fire, killing eleven students and an instructor. All campus activities are suspended for a week, and during this time you hear a rumor that he left behind a video the FBI will not release. Barbara Walters comes out of retirement to interview the father of the shooter on prime-time television. News teams book every hotel room in the city limits, and everyone keeps saying "tragedy" with such vague disdain, as if the shooting was just a mad dream, not some kid adding his personal darkness to a collective shadow that had already spread across our lives. Still, at night, when you overhear prayers about evil conduits, you clasp your hands and listen. You sleep with the blinds closed and the fluorescent lights on.

When the university publishes a list of the victims, you find out that one of them is Casey Bishop—Eddie's wife. You go online to confirm this, and find a picture of three people on a hiking trip, standing with their backs turned to a bluff line somewhere in the Ozarks. One of them is unmistakably Eddie, with his precise beard and thin, flyaway hair. The other two people you don't know. Me, with an overblown smirk, the kind that now belongs to an abandoned version of myself. And Casey, wearing a billowy sweater, bangs cutting across her eyes. She's bearing her teeth like she is half smiling, half preparing to battle the stranger we asked to take the photo. You look too long and she becomes fixed, the way dead people become their own archetypes, how they take you back to the honeysuckle and azaleas and lichen-covered rocks and rolling hills that surrounded them. Back there, time is so habitable. It is infinite.

On the day campus re-opens, you want to walk to the English department to see if your paper will be there, wondering if Eddie graded them before all this happened. But you're afraid of campus—everyone is. Eventually, you rationalize that this is probably the safest the campus will ever be, so you walk onto the bright sidewalks, past a media cavalcade at the on-campus hotel, where news helicopters buzz overhead. Your paper is in a box on the floor with sixty others. There are a few sentences underlined, and on the back page scrawled in blue ink, Eddie has written THIS PAPER IS BEAUTIFUL. The irony of such a statement is not lost on you—it makes you think there is some critique embedded in it, like your paper is beautiful in the same way that the ugly girl is ugly.

So you walk back to your dorm, through a campus that has police officers leering down every corridor. Flowers and makeshift cenotaphs line the sidewalk. Ironwood trees shift in silence. Colors of the sky smolder against stone buildings. You decide you can't be here, so you walk off campus towards downtown. It is winter now. Week-old snow is piled on shady patches of grass, and puddles are icing over again in the absence of the sun.

When you cross Arkansas Avenue, you pass by my house, where Eddie and I stand in my kitchen, lit up in the front window like a giant fish tank. Normally, we'd be reading quotes from student papers, or talking about love like it's a cliff we're walking towards. We'd be overstating how lost and in debt we are, as if being small-town professors has granted us entry into some high and mighty misunderstood club. But today, we are marching around the empty cul de sac of the shooting. We are trying to talk about loss, though we haven't felt it yet. We've been feeling something else entirely. Something more like suspense.

At first, you think this coincidence means something, like the tragedy is circling around to explain itself. But nothing happens. Eddie takes a phone call. I sweep the floor. The window buzzes with empty light. So you keep walking, still with no destination in mind. Cresting one hill, you can see the far-reaching gray of leafless trees, undulating over hilltops and eventually into the delta where you'll spend the next month, because Christmas break is here. You expected college to take you far away from home and the person you were. Instead, it's like a roller coaster that disappeared before ascending its first peak, one that has left you staring down onto the world from a stranded place in the sky.

Nicola Griffith in conversation with Alexis M. Smith

Summer 2018 · Digital exchange

I was nineteen years old the first time I encountered Nicola Griffith's work. It was 1999. I worked at The Crumpet Shop in Pike Place Market, and on my breaks read books I found around the corner at Left Bank Books. *The Blue Place* was the first in a series of novels starring the most nuanced (and hands-down sexiest) queer woman crime fighter ever to appear in a literary thriller. I was an avid mystery reader, and an aspiring-writer baby dyke, unsure of whether there was a place for someone like me in the literary canon, and Nicola Griffith lit a way forward.

Griffith has published many stories and seven novels in multiple genres, won awards from the Nebula and the James Tiptree Jr. to the Washington State Book Award and the Lambda (which she has collared an impressive *six times*). She's a literary scholar and an activist, bringing vital critical attention to writing by and about people with disabilities. Her most recent novels are the highly-acclaimed seventh century epic *Hild* (a sequel, *Menewood*, is in the works), and *So Lucky*, a sharp, dark gem of a thriller, haunted by the manmade monsters that our current political reality has lured out of hiding.

Nicola Griffith and her wife, writer Kelley Eskridge, live in Seattle. We conversed over the summer, just after the launch of *So Lucky*.

Smith

What kind of reader were you, growing up? Do you remember the first book or books that made you want to be a writer?

Griffith

The same kind of reader most writers are, I think: hungry. I loved to read, and I read everything in reach. Literally. My local library as a child seemed to operate on the principle that if you could reach it you could borrow it. Or maybe it was just that they got confused about some historical writers who also sometimes wrote for children. Henry Treece, for example. He wrote some modernist historical fiction that's most definitely unsuitable for children—unless you believe casual sexual violence is appropriate—yet I read them when I was eight or so.

The books that made me want to be a writer? All of them. None of them. Every single book I've ever read has added to what I know of story and writing; those books made me the writer I am. But did any of them make me want to be a writer?

To me there's a difference between wanting to Be a Writer and wanting to write. I wanted to write early on; pinning down a description or a moment or a feeling felt like a triumph. I didn't decide to be a writer until I was in my twenties. Or perhaps it might be more true to say I didn't *realize* I wanted to be a writer until I was in my twenties. I had a dream about being at a fancy awards dinner, and winning, and waking up knowing it was the Booker Prize, and that I would win it one day.

Smith

Are there books you wish you could go back and read again for the first time? Or, conversely, are there books you read over and over again, for the readings that change with time? Who is in your personal literary canon?

28 • *Griffith*

Books I wish I could read again for the first time? None. I only reread books I love. And if I love a book why would I want to forget all the wonderful times I've had reading it so far?

The books I reread most consistently at the moment are Patrick O'Brian's Aubrey-Maturin series of twenty-plus novels that begins with *Master and Commander*. I've read the first thirteen a couple of dozen times. I used to reread *Lord of the Rings* once a year and gain a slightly different perspective each time. But it's now been five years and I find I'm not pining for it.

What is a literary canon? That's not a rhetorical question. Those novels without which our work might not be, or would certainly be different? Novels we admire? Novels we love irrationally and reread for comfort despite their glaring flaws? Exemplars to point students to? I don't know.

What I do know is that whenever I try to come up with a list it's very difficult to name books I love by and about women. There are plenty of works by and about women that I admire, but I don't love them; I don't reread them, buy them as gifts, or reach for them when I need to know how another writer does things. Why? Because they brim with suffering, rage, or the claustrophobia of domesticity and/or oppression.

The books I love are almost all set in the outdoors, preferably in nature. My old friends and favorites are books where things happen; characters who sit around thinking are boring. I love books with protagonists who have will and agency. I like high stakes. I need also a sense of the ineffable, a kind of wild magic, an almost pagan exhilaration. I like joy—hard times, too, of course, but as both writer and reader I subscribe to characters being vessels hollowed out by sadness in order to be filled with joy—not wry contentment but unbridled, blazing *joy*.

The first half a dozen Patrick O'Brian books are practically perfect—except they're by a man about men. Even though it's nearly fifty years old, I love Mary Stewart's *The Crystal Cave*; if Merlin were a woman I'd never stop talking about that book. Books that I think of fondly include Susan Cooper's *The Dark is Rising*, Rosemary Sutcliff's *Sword at Sunset*, but they're all about men (or boys).

The women who write about women whose work I admire and is set outdoors—Joanna Russ, Suzy Charnas, Vonda McIntyre, Octavia Butler, Elizabeth Lynn—are often built around a kernel of rage and depend on the struggle with some kind of oppression. They are often, though not always, more playful at shorter length; this is particularly true of Russ.

This is one of those thoughts that to explore fully I'd have to reiterate my doctoral thesis, so I'll stop there.

Smith

You've recently earned a PhD. I imagine that has changed your reading life—or, at least it did for awhile? And what about your writing? Have you noticed a significant difference in either your practice or your experience of the writing? You already seemed to have a healthy relationship with research, both historical and practical (I feel I could almost manage a cabin renovation after reading *Stay*), but I wonder whether that has changed for you?

Griffith

Doing a PhD has given me a deep and visceral aversion to difficult fiction. I'm not talking about intellectually challenging fiction, fiction that requires focus, or goes deep into unexplored territory, because none of that feels difficult if it's interesting. But it has to be interesting. After an entire year of forcing myself to read books I did not care about for their own sakes, I am now quite sure that the only challenging novels worth reading are those that arrest and fascinate me from page one. It's not worth being challenged for not-fascinating books. Conversely, I'm perfectly happy to read fast shallow books that tell me nothing new as long as they entertain and don't actively annoy me for a couple of hours.

I no longer read most It Books because most not only are not very well written but say nothing interesting. I'm no longer willing to read as a duty. I'm happy to struggle if I think something's worth it—I'll still read horribly written, badly typeset early medieval research, for example—but I won't read so-called Literary Novels that promise to be depressing.

I still love researching—though so much early medieval research material is best read on a physical page, and so many of those books are not only huge but heavy. While writing *Hild* it was my habit to sit on the deck surrounded by flowers and bees and hummingbirds, with a pile of dense, foot-noted books, and tell myself I was working... But now I have to prop heavy books on a sturdy bookstand, which means indoor reading only. And now it's harder to pretend I'm working when just basking in nature...

Smith

A couple of years ago I came across a Joanna Russ story, "Souls," (published in 1982) which begins: "This is the tale of the Abbess Radegunde and what happened when the Norsemen came." It's a riveting, raging, page-turner of a story—not at all what one might expect from a historical story about an abbess. What's the opposite of historical romance?—it's that. It immediately brought to mind *Hild*, not simply because both stories take place in Britain in the early Middle Ages, but because of the way both stories are so *alive* in time and place. The characters live on the page through their actions and interactions, even while the stories themselves are tethered to deeper philosophical and mystical questions. And violence has its own language for the characters of both stories. Can you talk about the role of violence in *Hild* and your other novels? Is it an expression of that "kernel of rage," you're drawn to?

Griffith

I'm not drawn to rage. The opposite, in fact. I yearn for books by and about women who do things, who have agency in the great outdoors, but who aren't angry. Books by and about women that are full of rage are often too focused on what women can't and don't have, what they can't and don't do, as opposed to what they do and why, and how they think, and why. It's why although I admire those novels I mentioned it's the shorter, more playful fiction that I love and reread.

Russ's short fiction is a perfect example. "Souls" is the first piece in *Extra(Ordinary) People*, which is a marvelous collection: whippy and bright and so sharp you laugh as you realize you're bleeding out. One of the things I enjoyed about "Souls" was Radegunde's clarity, her ability to think, to assess and manipulate others rather than constantly re/acting from fear. In that sense I see some similarity with Hild, though Hild of course is perfectly willing to fight physically as well as verbally. And Hild is much less convinced of her superiority; she isn't weary the way Radegunde is (though perhaps that's a function of their relative ages). Probably my favorite story in that book, though, is "The Mystery of the Young Gentleman," which is sharp, witty, genderqueer science fiction. But we are talking about Russ, so that's not all it is. It's pulp adventure fiction, with sex and gunplay and gambling, money and reversals and danger. Also a parody of Victorian porn. And, literally, a comedy of manners. Exhilarating stuff. And no rage, no violence.

With two exceptions the violence in my books is not about rage. The exceptions are *So Lucky* (which is so different from anything else I've done that it needs its own interview) and one brief scene halfway through the middle Aud novel, *Stay*, when Aud's grief overwhelms her and she loses her shit. Apart from that one scene, Aud's violence throughout three novels is wholly naturalized: she's a force of nature, as impersonal as a lightning strike. She's violent in the way anyone dealing with the criminal underworld is violent: violence is one tool among many, but one her opponents understand. Unlike most violent women in crime fiction Aud is not an avenging angel, a protective family member, or in twisty psychological torment. She uses violence because she can; it's efficient.

Aud loves life, is wholly engaged in her environment, built and natural. Her violence is part of that love of life, her visceral delight in herself and her world.

Hild's the same: she loves the world because she understands it; she understands it because she spends time with it; she spends time with it because she loves it. Like Aud—like me, really—she's a creature of the body. She learns through her body: through what she smells and sees and hears. I think this is what many readers mean when they say it's immersive and alive: it's the sensory detail. I link the world to her body: we experience the world through her. Not just her senses but her responses to those inputs: the adrenaline surge, the sickening lurch of danger, the flood of saliva at the scent of roasting pork. It puts us there with her. No, it puts her inside us: her experiences and dreams and lessons are ours. Because she belongs in her world, we belong, too. She lives in a time when might was right; she doesn't think too much about violence one way or another; it's just the way of the world. And like Aud, she's smart and pragmatic: if violence works, use it.

As with Aud, my hope is that the reader learns to think as Hild does, and respond that way, just a little.

So Lucky also deals in rage and struggle. The protagonist Mara says, "Anger is a strange beast… It's a physical thing that needs physical remedies." She contains a kind of fury at injustice that propels her to fight for the vulnerable, to be direct with colleagues, to face conflict head-on, sometimes by acting without thinking. But we're also privy to Mara's deepest fears, which haunt her to the last pages of the book (spoiler alert, I guess?). The ending gave me chills: where some mysteries have been solved, the monster remains. Mara has multiple sclerosis, known as "the monster," among some with MS, but there's more to it than the literal interpretation. That made me wonder about the relationship between fear and anger, as primary sources of conflict in stories. Is the greater tension of the story actually in the fear, which has no remedy? Is there a similar tension between violence and vulnerability?

Griffith

So Lucky is the first book I've written that is overtly about the nexus of fear and rage. It's the first book I've written that is explicitly about an Issue (ableism in this case). I'd be surprised if they weren't related. The core of *Lucky* is not fear, vulnerability, or rage; it's about helplessness and whether you go gently into the good night or not. Are you willing to believe you belong in the crappy little box they put you in—the story of how cripples can't have or don't deserve a real life? Or are you going to tell a different story? It takes Mara a long time to figure out she's been sold a pack of lies about disability—as we all have—but she finally gets there. That's the problem with implicit bias; it's insidious. You have to recognize it in yourself, recognize how it controls your responses to the world, before you can root it out. And even when you do see it, it's not always possible to extinguish it. Implicit bias is like a retrovirus; you might think it's gone but it's always there, waiting to flower at unexpected moments. That's the monster, not Mara's physical impairments.

Many writers use fear as the springboard for story. It can be useful. There again, hunger—for sex, power, belonging—also works pretty well. It just has to be a good, clear emotion.

I'm curious about your aversion to "It Books" and whether you find literary-novels-of-the-moment depressing because they avoid the kind of tension and conflict we're talking about here? Is that why they seem depressing? Because they don't engage in the urgency of action and violence/vulnerability and fear?

They make me impatient because they don't engage in anything meaningful in a wider context. The big wide world and the people in it *matters*. Really, who apart from you gives a shit about the ethics of you having an adulterous affair? Or your inner conflict over whether or not you should feel bad about not having a baby? Or whether your dinner party will turn out well enough to be discussed positively in your social circle? No one will die one way or another. The world won't change. You probably won't even lose your job or home. It feels pointless. That kind of insipidity makes me want to reach into the book to, say, the privileged, self-absorbed drugged-up deliberately somnambulistic protagonist, pour cold water on her as she wallows in her own high-thread-count existential misery, and yell, *Grow the fuck up!*

A lot of It novels are depressing. They're depressing because they focus not on horror (or terror or lust or joy or hunger) but on angst, anxiety, and self-worthlessness. Anxiety and angst are not major, free-flowing emotions; they are a sign of internal dithering. Think of a novel's premise as an analogue of a self-defense situation. Fear sends a message as clear as a bell: *This situation is dangerous; get out now!* Anxiety is about second-guessing yourself: *It's not really dangerous, is it? Surely not. I know him; he's my husband's friend. I must be wrong...* When a character is constantly in that self-questioning mode, it makes me as a reader impatient and irritated. Why don't they believe themselves and just fucking get out?

I like fiction about people who are clear. How they deal with things can be nuanced, the situation can be complex, their histories can be Byzantine, but their emotions need to be clear; they need to know how they feel; they have to decide what to do. They can be wrong—in fact it's better if they learn, grow, change their minds, fuck up, etc.—but oh god they need to be *clear*. I hate characters who dither.

Smith

With each of your books I come away with a sense that for your protagonists, intelligence and awareness are at the center of their agency. I guess that's why I refer to violence as a language for them—one of many they speak. Hild, in particular, speaks or reads many "languages" of nature—we experience the world through her, as you say—and this ability becomes her superpower, but she's actually the earliest kind of scientist. (I have a friend, a practicing Wiccan who works in IT, who says, "I don't practice witchcraft, I practice witch*science*.") I feel like this is a shift in the paradigm of how women of her time are commonly represented, at least in literature. But I'm not an academic. (I've read Julian of Norwich, and that's about the extent of my experience with source texts anywhere close to Hild's time.) As you researched *Hild* (and the sequel, *Menewood*) what surprised you most about the time—about the roles of women or anything else?

Griffith

You and I are closer to Julian of Norwich's time than Julian was to Hild's—Hild was born 1400 years ago; her world was more different to Julian's than I think ours is to Julian's.

We know so little of Hild's time. The Anglo-Saxons were not literate in the way we think of it today. Some specialists would have had knowledge of runes, but from what little material evidence we have, they were used mostly as inscriptions rather than communication. Power, influence, and the administration and buttressing of same, would have worked quite differently. Law worked differently, kinship worked differently; war, land ownership, religion, allegiance: all different. Before the influence of Judeo-Christian (via Greek misogyny) values, who knows how women were regarded? I certainly don't because those writing everything down could not see past their own bias.

All I knew was that the role of women in the so-called Dark Ages could not remotely resemble the bullshit we've been fed in which we were merely rape toys and/or brood mares and/or warty old wise women of the wood. Because otherwise how could Hild—born the second daughter of a murdered father, with zero power and influence in the regime of petty warlords styling themselves kings of a feuding, bloody, aliterate, heathen culture—end up counselor to kings of proto-states with a literate, Christian bureaucracy; a teacher and leader of bishops; head of a religious foundation famous for its influence and hosting of the Synod which changed the course of British history; and still known fourteen hundred years (nearly a millennium and half!) later for her power, wisdom, and learning?

Clearly there was a lot going on about which was know nothing. So to write *Hild* I had to unimagine the last 2000 years of gender discourse. And then I had to reimagine it. But to do that, I had to build the entire seventh century, and to do *that*, I had to know what was known. So I researched every single fucking thing about the late sixth and early seventh centuries I could find; I research for 15 years. Climate data, analysis of skeletal remains (human and animal), jewellery, metallurgy, agriculture, flora and fauna, building techniques, charcoal manufacture, and textile production. Especially textile production. Fairly late in the process I learned that, by one estimate, Anglo-

Saxon women spent 65% of their time on textile production. Think about that: more time on cloth than on sleeping, childcare, and food preparation combined.

Textile production was the tech industry of the seventh century: it lay at the heart of everything. And given the evidence of language, women owned it, in every settlement from farmstead to royal vill. That single fact must have influenced every aspect of life, just as it influenced the novel.

Smith

I felt the same way with Aud—who is in many ways the model of the noir detective, but whose relationships—especially with other women— suggest questions about the sexism that permeates some detective fiction. Aud seems baffled by women who don't claim their own agency, but you subtly turn notions of women as the weaker sex on their heads throughout the series. Can you talk about what it was like creating Aud as a character in a long line of mostly male detectives? What questions, if any, did the process bring up for you about the genre?

Griffith

So much crime fiction, whether mysteries, police procedurals, hardboiled, noir, cozies, or thrillers, is about the status quo: restoring it by solving a murder; operating outside it, in the case of maverick PIs; shoring it up in terms of the international order for spy capers and thrillers; watching it spiral down the drain in terms of noir. In the crime fiction I read, written in the second half of the twentieth century by men about men, the pro- tagonists never changed. To a degree they still don't—think of Lee Child's Jack Reacher. When men wrote about women, women were (and often still are) victims—either already dead or alive and being abused. When women started writing about women, we were still the victims, only sometimes now we were also protectors of sisters or children and/or avenging angels.

Best case scenario? The female protagonists were full of self-doubt. Or tormented alcoholics, or gamblers, or had problems with impulse control. Or they lacked self-esteem, or were terrified of their own strength, or some damn thing. Some of these women did grow and change, but they were all damaged. There were no competent and confident women who rescued, saved, and protected people just because they could. And they enjoyed their job. That's what I wanted to see: women as White Knights riding to the rescue Just Because.

I wanted to write a woman as the flawed (but not damaged) hero: James Bond, Travis McGee, Spenser. Why hadn't anyone done that? I could see a way to do it, so I did.

What delighted me about writing Aud was how easy it is to create a character when you're not simultaneously world-building. There's so much *room*! As with fictional world-building you can still do three things at once with every scene—or line of dialogue, or even sentence—but it can be mood and character and plot; it doesn't have to weave in any explanations/ explications about how a society works. It's just... the world. It was delicious. So my question for the genre is, basically, given how fucking easy it is to write character in this genre why had no one before managed to come up with a real woman who revels in being a real hero??

Smith

I read on your website that you've regained the rights to the Aud novels (from three different publishers), and you're hoping to reissue all three (*The Blue Place*, *Stay*, and *Always*) and (eventually) to write another in the series. You say, "I'm very fond of Aud and her story; I love writing her." I, for one, love reading Aud, so it didn't surprise me to hear that. I feel like writers have a tendency to concentrate on the angst, and on the frustrating parts of the creative process (I'm certainly guilty of it). Can you say something about the love of writing a character, and, perhaps, the joy of bringing a character to life itself?

Griffith

Aud came from a dream: a naked woman sleeps sprawled, confident as a lion, on the brand new carpet of an utterly bare apartment. She's the first to move into the whole complex. It's hot. Orange sodium light slices through the blinds across her hip and cheek; tree frogs churr. There's a click, and she flicks open her eyes to find a man pointing a gun at her. And in my dream this woman doesn't wait for him to speak she just rises off the floor in one fluid motion, old-fashioned Maglite flashlight already swinging in her hand, and, crack, breaks his neck. Just like that. From the first click of the gun to the intruder lolloping down onto the carpet like a sack of potatoes: two seconds.

I woke up thinking, *Whoa!* Then I wondered: *What kind of woman could do that—no hesitation, just the right thing, instantly?*

I didn't know. I had trained for years in martial arts and self defense; I'd been attacked more than once; defended myself more than once. Yet the one time I'd been woken from a sound sleep by men threatening to break down the door, rape me, and set the house on fire, I froze for at least 20 seconds before I could respond (though it felt like about a year). It would be lovely if we could respond instantly but mostly people can't and don't. So who could this woman be? How could she have become like this—without being damaged?

I was writing another novel but this question was always in the back of my mind as I worked. Then one day I went to the library just to browse while Kelley picked up a couple of things she's ordered. I found a book from the 60s about Norwegian architecture. Nearby was an even older book in a plain blue binding: Norwegian history. I leafed through it, and came across a woman, called Aud the Deepminded, born in the ninth century. *Huh*, I thought. *She must have been pretty special to be remembered as the Deepminded 1200 years later.* And, *Oh*, I thought. *Oh.* The woman in my dream was Norwegian. And she was called Aud.

So now I knew who she was not how she had become herself.

I spent three books finding out and it was an almost ecstatic experience. Aud takes so much delight in her skills and in the world in general; she loves life. And at the same time she can be startlingly dense about other people, particularly women. She is constantly baffled by why other women don't just say what they mean, and act from confidence and conviction. Why do they worry so much? I had a good time with that. Actually, I had a good time with just about everything in those books. I think it will be marvellous to get back to Aud and see how she's getting on in the brave new world. When *Always*, the third novel, came out, Twitter did not exist. Amazon was only 10 years old. Seattle was just entering the Great Recession. Oh, I am going to have the best time!

One thing I'm seriously looking forward to is narrating them as audio-books. I've always loved to perform—first with music and now with novels. I'm one of those authors that actively enjoys reading aloud in public and talking to readers. But until *So Lucky* I'd never been in a studio to record anything but music and radio interviews. Narrating was an astonishing experience: feeling the work take flight, take shape, take form clothed in the power of the human voice. I loved it. I used to love reading aloud from the Aud books—those books really are designed for voice—so I can't wait to bring Aud alive that way.

I'm hoping to do that with Hild, too, when I finish the sequel, *Menewood*.

I wanted to narrate the first book, but the publisher wouldn't take a chance on a beginner with such a big book. But now I'm no longer a beginner…

Smith

You also seem to love writing about the landscape. When writers don't bother to describe the flora and fauna or the climate of a setting accurately, or at least vividly, I lose trust in the narrative as a whole. (Even if I don't know the particular landscape, I want to get the sensory experience of it.) You write not just precisely, but lyrically and reverently about the natural world in your books. In *Hild*, you were imagining or recreating a world that, as you say, is very far removed from ours, even in climate (and, as I think about it, in the amount of species die off since her time), and in *Ammonite*, you create a landscape on another planet. In each, there's a lucidity to descriptions of the environment that is integral to the story. Do you have a sense of where this inclination toward getting the landscape right comes from, for you?

Griffith

Natural landscape has always been important to me. I grew up in a big family in a crowded city. The only time I ever had to myself was outside. As a toddler apparently I had a tendency to escape from the house and head for the woods. Combine that with other in-born tendencies—to not sleep much, and to refuse any kind of confinement, including clothes—and we end up with a three year-old walking naked down a city street at dawn on the way to the closest semi-wild bit of land. The Hiding of the House Keys became more and more difficult for my parents as I learnt to climb on furniture and ferret out even the most cunning nooks and crannies. And then somewhere around four years old I began to understand this Obey Your Parents thing, or perhaps my parents worked out that if you put a bolt on the door right at the top, even a four year-old who's managed to drag a table to the door, plus a chair to get onto the table, can't quite reach it…

But the happiest memories I have of childhood are outside under the sky very early in the morning. Every year we used to go on holiday to the same house on the coast, and I would wake before anyone else and go stand on the edge of the cliff, and just breathe as the light broke over the sea. As soon as I was allowed to go hiking with friends we went to the Dales and the North York Moors: lovely!

The first short story I wrote with the goal of publication, "Down the Path of the Sun," (which ended up being the fourth story I published) was just an excuse to describe the landscape of the Norfolk Broads and how at dawn the rising sun lays down what looks like a red-gold path on the water to the horizon. I wanted to travel that path…

Smith

I know you have lived in different countries and climates, but you've been a resident of the Pacific Northwest for many years. How has the landscape of the Northwest influenced your writing?

Griffith

The biggest change for me regarding landscape in my writing came when I moved from the North of England to the American South. In the North I'd been very physically fit so my perspective on nature was very much that of someone moving through it. In the South, I got sick with what was eventually diagnosed as multiple sclerosis, which slowed me down a lot. Plus, it was hot and sticky. So I spent much more time just sitting under the trees or by the water and looking. That's where I learned to observe minutia: the mica glittering in the dirt; the way water boatmen dimple the surface of the water as they skate across the pond; how peeling paint has a tendency to break into an epithelial pattern. On days when I wasn't well enough to get outside, I would lie on the sofa and watch the quality of light change as it tracked across the tile, then rug, then wooden floor, then up the textured walls.

I'm not sure how moving to the Pacific Northwest has changed my work, except perhaps to help me see just how extraordinary the South is in terms of lushness and color. I couldn't have written *The Blue Place* until I left Atlanta and held those semi-tropical colors of my memory against the watercolor wash of green, blue and grey that is the PNW. The PNW is both very fertile and welcoming—the creeks and temperate climate, the sea shore, the endlessly changing sky—and oddly monotonous. For example, on my last visit to the Ho Rainforest it was weirdly quiet under the trees apart from the repeated call of a single Junco. The problem as I see it is that the ecosystem lacks animal diversity because the big predators—lynx, wolves on land, bears by the river, and orcas in the sound—are either wholly or mostly gone, and the medium predators—such as fishers on land, and sea lions and salmon in the water—are increasingly rare. Bring those back and things would change.

The climate of Seattle is very similar to that of Leeds where I grew up: temperate, moderated by a warm marine current, and partially in rain shadow. Not too hot in the summer, not too cold in the winter. Yes, there are miserable stretches in both cities where you really need air conditioning (which we installed in the first house and every subsequent house we've ever bought), and miserable stretches where many of us might sacrifice a relative just to make it stop raining; and, yes, there's very occasional cracking cold; but normally it's a fecund place hospitable to life—it's really not hard to grow flowers, fruit and vegetables. These days I don't do much gardening, so we stick to herbs and flowers, but they bring hummingbirds. Hummingbirds! They are belligerent little things but every single time I see one I feel as though life is a gift. How can the world be beyond redemption when there are hummingbirds in it? Like really fine fiction, they give me hope for the future.

—<o>—

On Learning the Galaxy Take Both Cash and Credit

Kelli Russell Agodon

I admit when I've had a little too much
to drink I love our inadequacies.

The pockets of the universe do not hold us—
like coins we slip through its unraveling seams.

Don't pretend the universe isn't unstitching itself
from our anxieties, it's tired of the party dresses

we made from waxwings, how we suck up the sea
just because we want a little salt on our lips.

It's true last week I learned I had money
in Idaho, though I've never been to Idaho,

there are states we avoid—*manic, delusion,*
confusion—I've got portfolios in all the capitols,

I've bought Boardwalk with two donuts
and broken whistle.

I'm standing on the corner with my top hat
and a sign: Will write poems for cashmere.

My hands in the universe's pockets
trying to collect its last dime.

—<o>—

Close Encounters

Jessica Mooney

When the last one leaves Eliza, she is dreaming of alien abductions. She stands in a cornfield, barefoot and alone, bright blue lights beaming down from overhead. She is topless, her breasts heavy with milk, her nipples chapped and sore. A friend once stuck cabbage leaves in her nursing bra to help soothe inflammation. She looked down to find a white apron is tied around her waist, the cheap kind found in drugstore French maid costumes around Halloween. If there's a dress code for Martian kidnappings, surely she's violated it. *Flying saucer*, she tries to say, but the sound doesn't come. *Flying saucer*. What it is, the name of it—how absurd. Her body shakes with all the times she's tried not to crack up laughing. The skin from her breasts starts to peel, falling to the ground in thin, green layers. A strong wind kicks up, tearing through the field, folding everything into itself like paper. Crumpled stalks, scarecrows with arms bent skyward in surrender. The earth rumbles and starts to swell, the ground vibrating like a tuning fork. She tries to run, but running turns into a river, which turns into drowning.

Then, the bright blue lights vanish; the wind goes too. The way it's all gone at once, in a salvo of crude theatrics—Cue flying saucer exit!—a lever pulled backstage at a student play. Somewhere there's a voice: *When the green men come for you, your hands will be two fists that won't open.*

Eliza's eyes open to a strange ceiling. Embers of blue light trailed in the darkness, the wind's chill prickled her skin. She shakes her head free from her dream and looks over at the lump next to her. Charlie. Rolled up in a blanket, mummified in dreams. It scared her the way his body committed to sleep, radically, immune to middle of the night churn. She was the opposite—she couldn't remember the last time she didn't wake up during the night. On their first date he'd asked what superhero power she would most like to have.

Sleeping, she'd said.

Something buzzes under her head. Earthquake? Panic shoots through her chest. She and Charlie had just moved to Seattle, a city long overdue for a seismic catastrophe of apocalyptic proportions. For a moment, she couldn't remember if she was awake or if this was just Act II of the dream, the part where Charlie sits up in bed and unzips his face, revealing that he's been an alien all along. That would explain a lot. His infinite patience, the way he picked her dirty clothes out of the laundry and smelled them, inhaling deeply. Another buzz, followed by a jolt. Then she remembers—James. She digs under the pillow for her phone. A quick swipe sends it flying off the mattress and clattering across the wood floorboards. *Shit*. She rolls over onto her hands and knees, frantically sweeping her arms in the dark. The mattress was on the ground—no bed frame, no pillowcases—a sheet draped lazily over the top in her and Charlie's exhaustive state, arriving past midnight, after three long days of driving. Her phone buzzes again, close by, send-ing a faint tremor through the ground. She lurches toward the sound, a dull pain throbbing in her lower back. She waits for another quiver of the phone, but nothing.

The apartment is little more than a collection of her and Charlie's conjoined possessions huddled in the dark, packed away in liquor boxes. In the dim light, they tower in silhouette like the skyline of a miniature city built by booze magnates. Jim Beam University, Bacardi City Hall. Slowly Eliza stands, her muscles cramped and achy from lifting and carrying stuff from the U-Haul up three flights of stairs. Staggering with her arms out, zombie-like, through the unfamiliar space, she feels around for clothes to throw on over her tank top and underwear. She stumbles over a pair of sweatpants—Charlie's—and pulls them on and tightens the drawstring. She steadies herself against a tower of boxes and finds a T-shirt strewn over the top. She throws that on, too.

Turning around, she kicks a small object with her foot and it slides away. She bends down and her fingers find her phone. 2:20 in the morning; two missed calls, both from the same unknown number. Her eyes now adjusted to the dark, Eliza made her way to the bathroom, stepping around the boxes, careful not to wake Charlie. She closes the door quietly and flips on the light. Her eyes flinch against the brightness. Two toothbrushes sit in an empty Starbuck's cup acquired at a rest stop off I-94. She splashes cold water on her face and tries not to think of the pressure in her abdomen. A balloon slowly swelling and pushing against her lower back. Droplets of water drip from her chin and snake down the drain.

"I'm pregnant," she says to the mirror, knowing she wouldn't be for long. She'd been through this before. This time she hadn't bothered to tell Charlie—hadn't bothered to tell anyone. But by saying it out loud, she announced its presence before it was gone, even if she was the only one to hear it. It was only right to acknowledge it had existed, this liminal clump of cells, however briefly. That it had been part of the world. A tiny flicker.

Outside, a damp breeze shuddered through the trees. Pine and spruce limbs swayed drunkenly, casting monstrous shapes in the night. It had been three months since her brother disappeared. But now, early October, was about the time of year he made his way up the West Coast to Alaska, an annual pilgrimage he never missed, no matter what the voices told him. Two weeks before she and Charlie left Indiana, James called from an unknown number to say he was heading to alien country. He'd met a guy online who was building a super telescope that could see all the way to Andromeda. James was going to stay with him for a while in a town just outside Roswell to help finish it. The plan was to take the telescope up to Alaska for meteor shower season.

She dials the missed call number, her heart pounding as it starts to ring. She and Charlie had found a rental in Wallingford, a quiet Seattle neighborhood lined with spacious craftsmen and Tudor homes. Yellow sconces with motion sensors light up garages and lawns as she walks past. The phone rings and rings, until the line cuts off and goes dead. Walking feels strange, as if her legs are stuffed with doll bunting. The red sliver on her phone screen shows 10 percent battery. God knows where she'd left her charger. She tries the number again, more ringing. Her stomach feels like a roof about to cave in. Eliza pushes it to a far corner of her mind. The spotting had started the day before, bright red blood. The real pain, she knows, won't come until later. The phone cuts off again.

She gets in her car and starts to drive down the block, shoving aside the fact that she has no idea where she's going. The dull orange glow of the gas light blinks on. Again, she dials. Each ring seems to stretch out longer and longer. *Where the hell was she going?* Her abdomen seizes and a wetness blooms into her crotch. She puts one hand down her pants and pull away a stringy red clot that clings to her fingers. She steadies the wheel with her elbow and reaches for a stack of Dunkin' Donuts napkins from the glove box. At the next stoplight, she shoves them all in her underwear. Just then, the phone stops ringing. There's a rush of air on the other end, and a man's voice comes through.

"Hello?"

—<o>—

Blinking is the first hello, the first magic trick. Everything here, then gone, then here again.

Each night, their mother hermetically sealed them into their beds. After two rounds of aggressive toothbrushing, she would scuttle Eliza and James to their room, their gums bleeding from her diligence. Their mother's wool slippers shuffled along behind them on the hallway carpet, a beige runway pockmarked with stains: a comet of bleach near the washing machine, the grape juice accident of 1984 by the linen closet. Eliza would inventory each one as she passed, a permanent archive of their mistakes.

Their mother would cite the Lord's Prayer as her fingers worked the mattress corners, her eyes bird-black in the dim light. Her hands shook as she stretched and tucked the sheets. No such thing as too tight. Even a little slack, and Eliza and James would slip away in the night. She smelled of mentholated cough drops and cold cream. She sucked on Halls to hide her cigarette smoke, but she and James could still smell it, a faint open secret. For all her praying their mother never said Amen, which always struck Eliza as funny. Wasn't *Amen* the most important part? The part that made it all stick?

Afterward their mother would stand outside and listen until she thought they had fallen asleep. Through the crack in the door, she and James could hear the tiny rattle of cough drops against their mother's teeth. They didn't dare speak. They just lay there, motionless in the dark, pinned to their beds like asylum patients. She buried them alive, so they learned to play dead. Fraternal twins in identical twin beds, their room an external womb, their breath finding each other in the dark, syncing each rise and fall of their chests. Eliza stared up at the ceiling and practiced twin telepathy, sending her brother set-ups to jokes through a dizygotic phone.

Why did the chicken cross the road?

What do you call a cow with no legs?

For years she fell asleep waiting for him to return a punch line.

—<o>—

James did eventually start to receive dispatches, but not from her. He was bussing tables after school at a Greek diner when he got the first transmission from a packet of Sweet n' Low.

James was bent over the counter wiping up a small pool of souvlaki grease when he heard a tiny voice emanating from the condiments. He looked down at the sugar caddy fanned with artificial sweeteners. The Splenda and Equals were silent. He leaned in closer. In a pink envelope of aspartame, a live wire crackled with static, like a radio station just out of range.

This is the 94th Aero Squadron, the voice said. *Give them our names. Say we are among the missing.*

—<o>—

"Hello?" The man has a baritone voice, a cowboy warmth.

"Yes, hello?" says Eliza. "I'm trying to get a hold of someone who called me from this number—my brother."

"Oh," the cowboy says. "Well, this is a pay phone and I don't see anyone around." His tone is sluggish, as if time moved slowly for him.

"Where are you?"

"Why?"

"Because I'm trying to find my brother."

"Find?"

"He's missing. He tried to call me from this number. I think. Twenty minutes or so ago."

"What's his name, this brother?"

"Please, can you just tell me where you are?"

The cowboy doesn't respond. A car horn beeps twice in the background.

"Hello?"

"You didn't say his name."

"James. My brother's name is James."

"You're shitting me." His voice brightens. "*My* name is James." He coughs violently. Something dislodges and he spits it out. "Wait... who is this? Vera?"

"Who's Vera?"

"Oh Lordy." The cowboy sighs deeply, blowing static through the phone. "There ain't enough quarters in the world for that story." A slight slur lapped at the end of his words.

"Could you please just tell me if you see a guy—pale and skinny, messy brown hair? He's probably wearing a gray hoodie."

"Listen, girlie. That's about every hooligan I met since I been here."

"Please. My brother—" Eliza bites her lip. "He's not all there."

The cowboy goes quiet for a minute. A rustle as he adjusts the receiver. "Tall kid, bit of a mumbler? Tattoo of an alien on his forearm?"

"Yeah, that's him." Eliza pulls over to the side of the road and sucks in a breath.

"I asked him about that—used to do ink myself, but that was..." he trailed off. "Saw him leave maybe ten minutes ago with another guy. Big, nerdy—looks like he speaks Star Wars."

"Where are you?"

"Listen, you're not gonna murder me or nothin', are you?"

"What?"

"It's a joke, kid," he says flatly. "7-Eleven parking lot up on Aurora, waiting for Triple A."

She pulls the phone away from her ear, the power bar a speck of red. There would be no way to GPS the location in time.

"Can you give me a cross street, maybe a landmark nearby?"

"Ah, let's see...7-Eleven just past the motel with the seal balancing a ball on its nose. Can't miss it."

She hangs up. Jagged cramps claw at her uterus. She lurches forward, gripping the steering wheel tight. *Please.* She sends out a transmission to see if anything comes back, to see if her dispatch gets through her brother's crowded brain. *Where are you?*

The first attempt was with their mom's Lady Bic. James didn't get too far into the skin before their dad came in from mowing the lawn and found the bathroom door locked, and locked doors were forbidden in their house.

Still, seventeen stitches. Their mom blubbered in the waiting room, clutching her rosary; their dad stood in front of a vending machine for over an hour, rubbing coins between his fingers.

Eliza stood over James in his hospital bed, staring down at the tiny black knots in his wrists and forearms. "One for each year of our lives," he said. James leaned over and blew air up and down the sutures. The fine hairs on his arms swayed gently. He smiled. "See, Lizard? Like birthday candles."

"Why did you do this?" she asked.

He shrugged and looked away. Faded pink curtains dotted with palm trees lined the window. "Why did the chicken cross the road?" he said.

The first one left her and Charlie two years ago. They were at a bed & breakfast overlooking Lake Michigan, a little getaway thrown in its honor. She stained the sheets red in her sleep. When they returned from urgent care, she and Charlie put on matching bathrobes and sat in Adirondack chairs overlooking the lake, a body of water so big they couldn't see the other side. *Shouldn't you be able to see the other side of a lake?* They deliberated, passing a bottle of wine back and forth. Red wine. The liquid sloshed in the neck as they sipped, and Eliza tried not to think of the bloody sheets balled up in the closet of their room. They opened another bottle, still trying to make sense of the endless body of water in front of them. By the time half of the second bottle was gone, she and Charlie had upgraded the lake to a smocean—a small ocean. Sip after sip, the two of them carried the joke aloft, stretching its mileage until it was thin enough to form a parachute. They didn't know how far the fall was, how high they had climbed in altitude over the course of two months, dreaming of their unborn child. They held onto anything they could to break the landing.

There would be another chance. Whatever this was, it was not meant to be their baby.

Good riddance, they'd said, drunk, full of feverish optimism. *Who wants an asshole who ghosts at its own party?* They laughed until the false bottom underneath cracked and split, dropping them into a dark silence that seemed like it would never end.

The second one left during a blizzard. More blood and a small piece of tissue the consistency of a raw chicken breast left behind in a Wal-Mart toilet. Eliza abandoned her cart outside the bathroom and drove for two hours to a town in central Indiana she'd never been to. She circled the parking lot of a T.G.I. Friday's with the windows rolled down. She shrugged off her coat then fumbled her sweater over her head as she held the wheel, stripped down to a tank top. Snow fluttered into the car, pricking her bare arms and face in cold little stabs. She felt blood seep through her jeans onto the driver's seat. Eliza promised herself she wouldn't stop circling until her lips turned blue, until she could imagine two of them gone instead of one.

Another blighted ovum, her doctor said. *The embryos attach but fail to develop. Then they just let go.*

Now the third one is on its way out. Eliza never told Charlie she was pregnant—she couldn't stand to see that look on his face again, the look that told her she wasn't capable of holding onto a life. This time, it will leave only her. She wanted the silence of it to crush her, to grind into the mortar of her bones until she turned to ash. But keeping it to herself felt no different than when people knew, when Charlie knew. With certain things, Eliza thought, even when you tell, it never stops feeling like a secret.

—<o>—

"Our first language was wolf," James said. "Do you remember?"

The second attempt is too many muscle relaxers. His body is riddled with small tremors that periodically quiver through his body. Aftershocks under the skin. A recovery side effect.

"What was my first word?" Eliza asked. Vertical blinds swayed gently in the breeze of an open window. Traffic hummed five stories below.

"It was more like an incantation." He tipped his head back and let loose. "Owwwww. Out-out-out-out-out-out-out-ooooooouuuut." After the howl, James fell quiet and turned away. A twitch of lightning fluttered at the corner of his mouth. "From the beginning, that's how I knew you would leave me."

Rain starts to freckle the windshield. Aurora Avenue, a road she'd driven in the U-Haul, is pitch black and smooth, mostly empty of cars. The drops fall faster and harder. Eliza speeds up the wiper blades and watches them slide back and forth in frenetic arcs, a manic kind of hypnosis. A string of titty bars and Korean barbeque joints passes by in neon smears along the side of the road. Her breath starts to gather on the windshield, fogging the glass. She blasts the defroster and squints out the window, keeping her eyes peeled for a seal with a ball on its nose. She'd forgotten to grab her glasses, which are still resting on the milk crate next to the mattress, next to Charlie.

Charlie.

She pushes him out of her mind and focuses on the road. A few stray cars pass. The orange gas light taunts her at every stop. And then, there it is, just like the cowboy said: a motel with a neon seal balancing a ball on its nose, the Sea Pearl Hotel—no vacancy. Eliza turns into the 7-Eleven just past it and parks. As she jogs toward the entrance, the napkins bunched together in her sweatpants, scratching at her inner thighs. A scraggle of teenagers linger under the awning, waiting out the rain. A beefy guy in combat fatigues unwraps a fresh pack of smokes and climbs into a white pick-up. No sign of anyone who looks like he might be payphone cowboy. The teenagers part as she brushes past. When she steps through the glass door, a bell announces her presence.

She sets a box of maxi pads on the counter to pay, and asks the girl behind the counter—a raccoon-eyed blonde with bangs styled into a hairsprayed claw—if she'd seen her brother. The cashier looks Eliza up and down and considers the description of James she'd given her. Eliza glances down at what she's wearing: stained sweatpants, Garfield T-shirt in tatters (used in a moving box to prevent wine glasses from breaking), no bra. She has on two different sneakers: one bright blue, one black; one hers, one Charlie's. The girl nods lazily. "Yeah, I seen him in here just a bit ago," she says, taking her money. "Fancied himself a ladies' man. Mentioned he was staying at the Motel 6 up the street." The cashier leans in closer. "Flashed his room key as he paid." She snorts and hands Eliza her change. "Asked me if I'd ever seen a meteor shower, and I'm like, yeah, baby, shooting stars every night."

—<o>—

James was planning to pass through Seattle the first week of October, right when she and Charlie were due to arrive.

"The three big beauties are all happening in the middle of the month," he said. "The Draconids, Taurids, and Orionids—not to mention the Northern Lights. Big John's almost there with the scope, but he doesn't understand infrared radiation."

"Well, why doesn't he come to you?" Eliza tried to picture her brother's online conspiracy theorist friends. A mobile of failed human experiments circled her imagination.

"You don't understand, Lizard. Big John's under federal surveillance by the FBI. He can only go as far as the Aisle 6 of the Pick and Save in downtown Lovington. He goes any further east, he's toast."

On her last day in Indianapolis, Eliza was supposed to finish packing up her life, run a dozen errands. Instead, she spent the morning pacing around the city, popping in and out of James's old haunts. The comic book store on Warren Avenue, the basketball court behind the Glendale Dairy Queen. Athena's, the diner where he used to work. Eventually, against all logic, she called the Lovington Pick n' Save. A young woman picked up the phone in the deli.

"Hello?"

Eliza asked her how many aisles there were in the store, and the deli girl released a world-weary sigh. "Listen, Frida, I don't have time for this shit. I got twelve pounds of pastrami to slice before 11."

"No, no—wait." She grasped for a reason to keep her on the line. "I'm with Pick n' Save Corporate. We're doing an annual audit of all our stores' square footage." Eliza bit down hard on her lip and heard the girl cover the receiver with her hand.

She came back on a moment later, forcing a bit more cheer. "Shit, I'm sorry," she said. "I'm new, so I haven't, you know, explored the whole place, but Rambo says we got seven aisles here."

"Hello?" Suddenly another voice came on the line, a young male. "This is Wendel Sanderson III. I'm the deli manager."

"Rambo?"

"Yeah?" he said, quietly.

She closed her eyes, immediately regretting the call, but she had to know. "What's in Aisle 7?"

—<o>—

Aurora Avenue. Sad casino after sad casino. Prostitution watch zones. Used car lots with large inflatable dolls, Gumby-like, air continuously blowing through them to make their limbs flail like homicidal epileptics. Bright lights in the rearview momentarily blind her. A large truck rides up close to her bumper and then changes lanes. Something catches Eliza's eye in the mirror. A streak of blood on her cheek, sweeping upward like a warrior's mark. She hits a speedbump going a little too fast, and another pulse of liquid seeps from between her legs. The sweatpants belong to Charlie. They would need to disappear if she can't get the blood out.

What if Charlie woke up and found her gone? What if he discovered one of his shoes missing along with one of hers? Eliza imagines him trying to piece together the disturbing puzzle of discordant shoes. She imagines blood trailing on the floor as he moves through the apartment calling her name, blood dripping from the moving boxes, the walls, a puddle by their apartment door, a flowing river leading to the outside, rushing around the block—a thick, red lagoon in the vacant spot where their car was parked. She imagines Charlie wading through it all, sweating, panicking. After a while, Charlie would inevitably give up, never knowing what happened. Charlie would move on, she tells herself. Yes, another woman would help him grieve. Her body would hold it all.

Eliza's chest tightens. She wipes away a few tears.

Charlie would never know where she disappeared to. Sitting with his head in his hands, sobbing until there's nothing left. Just two mismatched shoes in the darkness. He would eventually resign himself to the supernatural: she had simply melted into a pool of blood and vanished.

Number three was a sharper blade. A room with pale blue curtains frayed at the edges, James' wrists bound to a hospital bed with yellow plastic ties. Eliza tried not to look at his bright yellow cuffs and think of Hefty bags, trash that needed taking out.

"Why didn't you just devour me in the womb?"

She put her hands in the air and slowly moved toward the riot in her brother's brain.

"Because I loved you."

"Bullshit." He turned to the window but the curtains were drawn. There was no view. "You didn't even have a heart yet."

—<o>—

Charlie found a job in Seattle and thought a move across the country would do the two of them good. He thinks they need a new start. He doesn't tell Eliza that he thinks getting as far away as possible from Indiana is the only way anything can survive in her body. She doesn't tell him that the leaky container of her womb might be a sign that she doesn't get to have the kind of life other people are allowed to have, a life with kids and a house. A life with a family. She doesn't tell him about James's trip to Alaska, that he's expected to pass through Seattle, like a comet, any day now.

Instead, Eliza told Charlie she was fluent in 55 endangered languages, all of them understood by only one other person.

"Your brother," he murmured, a shadow crossing over his brow.

A U-Haul is the biggest vehicle either of them has ever been in. The rental came with its own Greek chorus for the driver: *How much room do I have?* Charlie guided the steel monster onto I-80, Eliza's body as still as a statue in the passenger seat. She was afraid to move, afraid pieces of her body might break off.

She counted the mile markers they passed. As distance accumulated, she realized she had already lost the ability to speak one language: Why the Chicken Crossed the Road.

—<o>—

The Motel 6 is just off an unpaved road, up a steep hill. No one expects to see a Motel 6 on a hill, lit up like a star atop a Christmas tree. The effect is elegant but misplaced in reality, a continuity error. Eliza thinks of the big lake she could not see across, the lake that was really a small ocean.

The car lurches forward and dies. Out of gas. The world is so quiet it seems like it's holding its breath. The rain has stopped. The black sky hangs loose and slack, a flat tire that needs filling. She steps out of the car and starts up the hill. She doesn't know what she'll say to James when she finds him. *Draconids, Taurids, Orionids*. The spidery names crawl around her brain.

She walks by gardens in the throes of fall, but the night, after the mist of rain, is warm like summer. It's a season she does not recognize. Thick green stems are topped with fireworks in bloom. Much of taxonomy is mysterious. She realizes she doesn't know the names of things. One by one, she calls out to the unknown. No language can name the box of little things that will not make their way out. Bibs and blankets suffocating in plastic packaging. She does not know what to call the grief of tiny spoons. She's lived among so much she's never named, swaddled in artificial intelligence.

As she walks up the hill, she imagines climbing up a long ladder that cuts through the sky and keeps on going. She gathers the strings of all the things that are not hers and lets them go, strings of refugee cells fleeing blighted ova. The others she ties to her wrist. Mine, she says, tying each string. *These are the things that attach. These I get to keep.* Lizard, the nickname her brother gave her. What it took to leave Indianapolis. Blood, thick and patient, spiderwebs down her thighs, her calves. All the languages will eventually bleed out into extinction. No single body can hold them all.

She looks up to the roof of the Motel 6. A shadowy figure moves across the sky. He stops and starts to set up what looks like a telescope. He extends a tripod, sliding metal poles out of their sleeves into a triangle. But then something is reconsidered, and the man retracts the metal legs and slides them back into a bag. He picks up the bag and walks away. *What if I lose him?* Not now, not when she's so close. She gathers her strength and starts running. She waves her arms. *James! Look at me!* She tries to shout but her breathing is too labored. *No… not now.* A few napkins ruffle out from the bottom of her sweatpants. She catches a glimpse of a dark wet stain as her foot passes over it.

Eliza watches the roof, hoping the shadow will reappear. A flash of light blinks in the sky, just above where he stood. *A plane? A star?* She will always be waiting for a certain kind of visitor. She pauses to see if it will flash again, and it does, but this time it stays bright. A tiny light. Here, then gone, then here again.

—<o>—

Beat or Beet?

Juleen Eun Sun Johnson

Is veggie a beat or a beet?

        A beet tongue?

Tongue of red.

        Red

                with velvet sighs.

Sigh of sighs.

        Cut the dark.

                Find

Find if you can

        still feel.

Feel the sharpness

        of the crawl.

                Or if the knife is dull.

If it can feel.

Red hallowed

Umbrella

Symmetrical

but in the end

never

after being blown

inside out

or maybe by design?

An instrument blunt and battered.

Half the beet laying on the freeway exposing its presents to the world.

—<o>—

Rhapsody No. X

Sarah María Medina

after Big God, Florence + The Machine

yo/ soy vidente/ yo/ see barrel of pistol/ pressed to your perfect/ crown/
yo/ sense cold steel/ pressed/ a mi tercer ojo/ yo/ pirouette across black
lake/ adorned with a blue silk gown// tú/ eres un/ Big God marching//
yo/ soy captured/ by light that flints/ off your reflection/ yo/ traipse sky/
roll my shoulder/ palm your crystal/ stick/ y rarely/ transcend yet/ tú/
keep me up at night// yo/ master flight/ trap wave/ tongue the gold grill/
of your other muse/ yo/ love her/ for taking/ all your sorrow// yo/ grasp
my own divinity// y no longer fear/ el otro lado/ de la isla/ yo/ survey
terrain/ for approaching diamondback/ y wait/ y wait/ y slide down/ to
cease/ yo/ slide down to fire// to regret is to cry/ to weep is to set free//
tú dices/ te amo/ te amo/ te amo/ to a stadium/ yet carry silence/ come
now/ my love/ how long before/ we death again?

―◇―

Revelations

Natalie Villacorta

People were looking forward to the eclipse the way teenagers look forward to losing their virginities. One million people were traveling to Oregon's Willamette Valley, where I lived, because it was in the "path of totality." There were no vacancies at the hotels in town, and no reservations available at the restaurant where I worked. My neighbor said she'd filled up her gas tank because traffic was supposed to be terrible and she'd heard rumors of fuel shortages. Some friends of mine were throwing a three-day-long party. They had purchased a bubble machine. All I had done was walk to the library for a free pair of protective eye glasses. I wasn't even sure about the difference between a solar and a lunar eclipse, and for a while, I didn't know which was happening. I had been meaning to read Annie Dillard's famous account of the 1979 total eclipse, but hadn't gotten around to it. My best friend Kathleen was visiting from Washington, D.C., and I was busy showing her a good time: whale watching, hiking, and gossiping about old boyfriends. Besides, I didn't get all the Dillard hype. All the writers I admired seemed to love her. One had even dedicated a book to her. But I got lost in her detailed descriptions of fields and stars and snow. I read whole paragraphs without comprehension. I reread them and they felt as unfamiliar as if I were reading them for the first time. I wanted people, their detailed thoughts and feelings. When the big day came, I still had not read "Total Eclipse."

—<o>—

Kathleen's visit lining up with the eclipse was a coincidence. She was on break from her graduate program, where she was getting her master's in theology. She was thinking that, after her program was over, she might become a nun. I struggled to understand how our lives had taken such different courses when we'd had similar upbringings. I, too, was in graduate school, but studying creative writing. I hadn't been to church except on Christmas in years. How had she ended up the religious one, when I'd been the one going to youth group for most of my teens? She attended a private school in our D.C. suburb, and I went to the public schools, but we'd known each other from a young age because our families belonged to the same Catholic church—we briefly played together on the parish basketball team, coached by her dad. But both our families stopped going to mass by the time we reached middle school. After that, I dabbled in several denominations—Evangelical, Episcopalian, Methodist—attending youth services wherever my friends and crushes were congregating. Every summer third through ninth grade, I went to sleepaway Bible camp in western Pennsylvania, and for a few weeks afterwards, I listened to Christian rock and prayed every day. Then my life grew busy with soccer practice and school, and my faith went into hibernation until the following summer. Kathleen, meanwhile, stuck to sports and student government.

But, after we graduated from high school, we traded places. While I went to the University of Virginia, lost my virginity, and avoided the many Christian ministry groups on campus, Kathleen took a gap year in Ghana, where she worked at a center for children with autism and Down syndrome, volunteered in an orphanage, and read the Bible in its entirety. When she returned from Ghana at the end of my freshman year, I didn't recognize her: She was thirty pounds lighter, her round cheeks flattened and stretched taut, her curvy figure transformed into straight lines and sharp edges. Also, she was devoutly Catholic.

I figured her newfound faith was just a phase, that her fervor would wear off, as mine had in the weeks following Bible camp. But her faith deepened. In college, she took religious studies classes, joined a campus Christian group, and saved herself for marriage. She did not try to convert me or judge me for my behavior, but I quietly judged her and felt judged in turn. She was brainwashed and backward. Because I didn't strive to live the way she believed was right, I assumed she saw me as morally inferior. Her commitment to a set of beliefs made me aware of how lacking I was in principles, and I didn't want to confront that truth. So, I avoided discussing religion with her, convinced that it would only doom our friendship. I accepted that, now, there was a part of her I would just never understand.

—<o>—

When I insisted on making banana bread the morning of the eclipse, even though it would make us late to the viewing party, Kathleen remembered that I'd wanted to read Dillard's essay. She offered to read it aloud as I baked. I agreed, predicting that Kathleen would like Dillard more than I had because they were both Catholic. I preheated the oven and collected ingredients from the cupboard. It was the night before the eclipse, February 25, 1979; Dillard was lying in bed in her hotel room in central Washington, staring at a forgettable painting of a clown. Not so forgettable, it seemed, because she was recalling plenty of details: his white face paint, his small laughing eyes. What did this painting have to do with the eclipse? A lawnmower buzzed outside, and I looked out the window. The sun looked no different than usual. A blur of brightness high in the sky. The earth looked the same as well. The grass was yellow from months without rain. I microwaved frozen bananas and crushed them. From the hotel, Dillard had driven to a five-hundred-foot hill, where it looked like people had gathered "to pray for the world on its last day," she said. I measured out a teaspoon of vanilla extract and splashed it into the bowl. I crushed walnuts with my fists and toasted them in a pan on the stove. I added white flour to my mixing bowl, and combined everything. Into the oven went the loaf.

The clock said 9:17 A.M. The moon was beginning to move over the sun, I knew, but I couldn't see anything different outside. I got dressed and brushed my teeth and Kathleen continued to read. Soon my skin would be silver, Dillard said. Soon Kathleen would look like a person in a black and white photograph. Soon I would hear screaming. I stopped brushing my teeth; riveted to the story, I wanted to hear every word. The screaming, Dillard said, would abruptly give way to silence. The sunny sky would turn navy like night and but amongst the stars would be something else, something strange: a silver wedding band, "a morsel of bone." Suddenly, I understood what everyone liked about Dillard. She made me feel like I was with her on that hill, almost forty years ago. I saw the world turn silver, then dark. I heard the screams and the silence. I felt my heart screech. I was with her as the world returned to its former state, as she streamed down the hillside and drove to a diner. I was with her as she ate an egg and sipped coffee, waking and remembering things as if she'd been asleep, trying to fit words to experience. She couldn't then, but later, in this essay, she had. She had found the words, and I wanted to hear them again, and so, when Kathleen finished reading, I asked her to repeat certain lines, not wanting the essay to be over.

The banana bread was beginning to smell sweet. I could continue to bake the bread until my fork, poked into the mounded center, came out clean, or I could pull the loaf from the oven, finish baking it at the party, and watch the moon slowly obscure the sun. I took out the loaf, wrapped it in white towels, and pushed it into my backpack, along with Dillard's essay. She had convinced me that witnessing a total eclipse would change my life and now, I didn't want to miss a moment.

—◄◦►—

When Kathleen told me she was thinking about becoming a nun, two years after her college graduation, I was not surprised. She had always done everything in the extreme—why be a vegetarian when you could be a vegan? Why bake a two-layer birthday cake when you could make a layer for every year of the celebrant's life, even if they were turning twenty-four? Most of my knowledge about nuns came from The Sound of Music; maybe, I hoped, Kathleen would be like Maria, who was attracted to the convent but discovered that her gifts were better utilized in a life outside its walls. Why would anyone want to vow to a life of poverty, chastity, and obedience? On the other hand, Maria's habit-wearing sisters had seemed pretty happy. If being a nun would make my friend happy, what did I care? Ever since she had moved back to D.C. and started her program in theology, she'd been happier than I'd seen her since high school. In college, she stressed over becoming a scientist and struggled with her body image, but now, she seemed to love her work, love herself. Before, we plodded through periods of silence when she was overcommitted with school and various clubs, but now she was as present in my life as she had been when we'd lived down the street from each other.

Around this time, I stayed over at her apartment one weekend and a snowstorm prevented me from returning home to the suburbs for several days. On the Sunday, she invited me to join her at mass. We went to the Basilica of the National Shrine of the Immaculate Conception, the largest Catholic church in the United States, because it was just down the street from her apartment in northeast D.C., and I'd never been. I was enthralled by the sparkling mosaics, the embroidered vestments of the priests, the hymns and prayers. It had been years since I'd been to mass, and it wasn't as boring as I'd remembered; in fact, it was compelling in its complexity. When we returned to her apartment building, we encountered two young men who offered to shovel our cars out of the snow for us. "For how much?" we asked. For nothing. They were Latter Day Saints, just out helping people in the example of Jesus Christ. Hearing this, I was prepared to shovel out my own car and was impatient to get inside the warm apartment. But Kathleen asked them where they were from, how long their mission was for, how their beliefs differed from other Christian faiths. I didn't listen to their answers. But I was awed by Kathleen's effort to connect—how the Mormons' beliefs were not threats to her own, but rather an opportunity to strengthen her own convictions and character. Was it God that made Kathleen so good? They shoveled out the car, and we brought them hot chocolate as thanks. I started to suspect that there was something to Catholicism, something for me. I wanted to be good like Kathleen, and maybe religion was the answer. I realized that I believed to be religious was to be ignorant, while being ignorant myself of religion. I decided to go to church.

—<o>—

We biked west, the sun to our backs. On a corner a few blocks from my house, a handful of people sat in lawn chairs with telescopes aimed east. They waved at us, we waved back. The green in front of the university— usually empty but for a few pedestrians walking along the center, tree-lined path—was clustered with people. They were all wearing protective glasses, staring up at the sun, riveted. What they saw was invisible to me. I felt the need to see it too. I pedaled harder. All around me, fixated on the sky, were people: In the parking lot outside the dorms, on the top tier of the parking deck, on the pavement outside the stadium.

"I have that feeling you get when you're going to the airport," I called over my shoulder to Kathleen, "like I'm going to miss my flight, even though I've left with plenty of time."

Normally, the four-lane road whistled with lumber trucks, but today there were no cars. We crossed without waiting for a signal. We passed people in the field of the elementary school, more people on the sidewalk.

We were nearly there—just a hill to climb, the hardest part of the ride. I downshifted, stood up from my seat. I was sweating, I was anxious, I was hung over and tired from partying late into the night. My legs ached. Halfway up the hill, I got off my bike and walked it the last two blocks. Outside the house where the party was already underway, we didn't bother to lock up the bikes. Even thieves wouldn't miss the eclipse.

—<o>—

I waited until I moved to Oregon for graduate school to try being Catholic because in Oregon I didn't know anyone. My new friends didn't know I wasn't really Catholic, and my friends and family who did know weren't around to judge me or say "I told you so" should I decide to quit. Mass—the music, the incense, the rituals—it all felt familiar, from my childhood, and yet I feared I didn't belong. Everyone else knew exactly what to say and do while I stumbled over the words to the Our Father and scrambled to sit or stand at the appropriate times. I longed to be like the other parishioners—to know, to believe in something, to be good.

On Sundays, I was excited to go to mass; I liked the singing, the quiet time for contemplation, the often-helpful homily. I introduced myself to the parish nuns and asked to spend time with them to see what Kathleen's life might be like if she chose their path, why it might appeal to her. The nuns were nothing like what I thought. They weren't old and stuffy and cloistered. They were young and wore Doc Martens and went for runs in the fields behind their house, their white veils fluttering behind them. I was struggling to adapt to my new unstructured life, and I envied their scheduled days full of purpose: prayer in their garage chapel, cooking, exercise, Bible study, mass. Perhaps if I became a believer then my days would be full of purpose too; I would never doubt that writing was worthwhile, full of conviction that I was God's mouthpiece on earth.

The nuns taught me how to pray the Rosary and gave me a delicate string of blue beads to keep. The repetition of the Hail Mary filled me with calm and, absorbed in the prayer, I often lost track of where I was in the chain, how many Hail Marys had gone by, how many were left. Mass was useful to me, the nuns were good, and I reported to Kathleen over the phone all that I was learning. I felt closer to her and hopeful that soon, I would be more like her.

But at the same time my Catholic curiosity was growing, I was developing feelings for another student in my graduate program. He was not Catholic, and despite growing up in a Methodist/Presbyterian church— whatever that was—he didn't even believe in God. It was getting harder to go to mass because on Sunday mornings, he was often in my bed. Either I left him sleeping there or he dropped me off at the church on his way home. While the other parishioners filed out of the pews and up the aisles to the altar to receive communion, I stayed kneeling and prayed for grace because you weren't supposed to take communion unless you'd gone to confession, and I hadn't gone to confession because I wasn't contrite about my sins. I was what the sisters called a Cafeteria Catholic, picking and choosing what beliefs I wanted to follow. God spat the lukewarm out of his mouth. I prayed for His help.

Our hosts, Patrick and Rebecca, a couple my parents' age whom I'd met through a family friend, and their other guests were already in the backyard, watching the screen of the sky, and they urged us to hurry; the show had begun. Patrick was a crop scientist; Rebecca was a retired high school science teacher. They were the kind of people who make their own pie crusts, decorate their table with flowers grown in their garden, freeze and can summer produce and eat it all winter long. This was why I'd insisted on baking banana bread from scratch; I knew a store-bought good would have been unacceptable, though they were too polite to ever suggest so. Also in attendance was one of Patrick's colleagues, a plant geneticist, her physicist husband, and Murray, their elderly neighbor. Kathleen and I put on our eclipse glasses and stared up at the sky. Behind their lenses, everything was black except for the sun, a cantaloupe-colored circle with a bite in the top right. The bite was the moon. We hadn't missed much.

In the grass, the physicist had arranged brightly colored bocce balls in the positions of the planetary bodies, our map to the sky. Mercury was closest to Earth, the physicist explained, but usually, we can't see it because when it's in our sky, the sun is high, blinding us to outer space. But perhaps today, we would see it. Venus, he explained, would be brightest, off to the right of the sun and moon.

The moon moved across the sun, and the world slowly grew dimmer. I was much more interested in the world than the sky. The yellowed light of day fading to a dusty gray. The plants in the garden—the basil, the joyful zinnias, the cauliflower with its stiff, long leaves and the squash with its wide floppy ones—looked alien, seeming to stretch toward the sky, just as eager for a glimpse of the eclipse as we were.

"It feels like we are on some strange planet," I said.

"We are," Rebecca replied.

As it grew darker, the air grew colder. A breeze passed over us. We counted down the minutes. We heard neighbors exclaiming with excitement, fireworks combusting and horns bellowing in the distance. The birds stopped singing; the bees ceased to buzz. The plant geneticist swore she saw the sunflowers move. For every living thing except us human beings, this was just another night.

The moon seemed to move so slowly and then, suddenly, totality was nigh. It was happening, and we all took off our glasses and stared directly at the ring of light in the sky. The corona, the crown, was white and glowing. It looked liquid to me. Like the moon had been dipped into glowing potion and some was dripping down its sides. "Murray! Take off your glasses!" Rebecca insisted. The old man must have been scared, but I didn't look at him to confirm, I didn't want to tear my eyes away from the sky lest I miss something. But I was not transfixed; each of my limbs was capable of movement. I attempted a photograph, but captured only a blur. To the right of the corona, I looked for Venus but could not see it. I searched for words to record in my notebook but my pen hovered above the page. Two minutes passed. I felt nothing out of the ordinary.

A diamond sparkled out from the top right corner of the crown—the sun, reappearing. I wanted to call out, "Not yet! Wait! Just a few more seconds." I wanted to feel something more. I wanted to feel dead, old, lost, anything at all. I wanted to think deeper thoughts, about things science cannot name—good and evil, how we care for each other though it makes no sense. But the diamond grew until I was forced to replace my glasses or be blinded. The world was black again, except for a slice of melon in the sky. Totality was over, and I was the same. I would not spend my entire life chasing the sight, like the umbraphiles—shadow-lovers—I'd heard on the radio. I was not dead, as Dillard had felt she was. The world had not ended.

—<o>—

When I left Oregon for my first Christmas break, I found one of my father's old gold crosses that he'd worn as a kid going to parochial school in the Philippines, and started to wear it. When I returned to Oregon, the nuns invited me to attend a weekly Bible study, and despite my misgivings about such a commitment, I attended the first one because I wanted to want to go. I was one of the only people under the age of forty, it seemed, and the other people at my table creeped me out: One kept rattling off the titles of books by various Catholics and asking if I'd read them, and another was sick with breast cancer and admitted she'd started going to daily mass only after her diagnosis. *Brain-washed, desperate for meaning*, I couldn't help thinking. I didn't go back, and I began to dread going to church. I preferred spending that time reading and writing, or even grading my students' papers, which I normally procrastinated on. I preferred to watch TV with my boyfriend. I started to skip mass and, when I did go, I was bored and consumed with thoughts about all I would do afterward. The gold cross was giving me a red bumpy rash so I stopped wearing it. I was increasingly doubting the Catholic \conception of God—why would He forbid some things that brought me joy? I was feeling like a fraud, my desire to be Catholic born out of my desire to have an identity, to have a purpose and to be told what to do. But Lent was approaching, and the parish priests said it was a good time to reflect on your relationship with God and try to improve it. I decided I was going to give Catholicism one last shot and take Lent seriously.

For Lent, I would read the Bible verses recommended by the fathers every day, pray, and write a reflection. In the nook where my refrigerator was nestled, I set up a prayer altar with candles and pictures of Christ. *Dear God, please open my eyes to You. Help me to see inside myself and discover my inner disorder, what inside of me rejects your love. Help me to understand your word and live it out in my life,* I prayed. I didn't stop having sex with my boyfriend, but when he left in the mornings, I lit the candles on my altar, made the sign of the cross, and told God my heart was open to His will. For my birthday, which fell in the middle of Lent, Kathleen sent me a package containing a glazed clay cross for my altar and a Miraculous Medal, a silver necklace with Mary's image that was supposed to help me receive God's grace. Kathleen had lit a candle for me in the Basilica and prayed for me. I thanked her; I needed all the prayerful help I could get. For the most part, I kept up my Lenten promise, and if I missed a day of reading the Bible and writing, I would make it up the next. But I suspected my diligence had more to do with my desire to procrastinate from my other work, that my reflections were a microcosm of why I was attracted to religion in the first place: I wanted someone else to tell me what was worth doing.

On Easter Sunday, I put on the Miraculous Medal and went to mass. This day was supposed to a huge celebration for Catholics, the day our savior was resurrected, but even in church, I just didn't feel God's love, or even His presence. As a last-ditch effort, I decided I would take communion, even though I hadn't been to confession, because what was the harm? If I wasn't a believer, then there weren't any consequences for bending the rules and, who knew, maybe the body of Christ was just what

I needed to feel him near. I shuffled up to the aisle hoping that, in the Easter crowd, none of the nuns would see me and judge me for taking undeserved communion. The wafer, with its Styrofoam texture, took a while to dissolve in my mouth, releasing a bland taste, like an oyster cracker, that comforted me. I waited for something to happen, a small sign to convince me to return to mass the next week. I thought about the brunch I was attending afterward, the promised mimosa bar. As the choir director announced the recessional hymn, I put on my jacket and slipped out to beat the post-church traffic.

—◁○▷—

After totality, we watched the moon move for a few more minutes, then grew bored. The plant geneticist began to wander the yard, looking for signs of change. She saw three bees motionless on the petals of a flower. We watched them as the world brightened. They began to stir. Finally, one took flight.

The solar system was collapsing. Venus collided with Mercury. The moon rolled down the hill and disappeared in the flower bed. The sun flew through the air, hit the earth, and came to an abrupt halt. The sun, the moon, the planets were just bocce balls again as we played the game. Our hosts prepared lunch. The banana bread went back in the oven. Occasionally, I replaced my glasses to monitor the moon's progress. It was slow; it had been slow at the start and was now slow to finish, but in between, the moon had sped. I felt guilty that something so rare was unfolding, and we were ignoring it.

As we ate lunch, we debriefed the main event. Kathleen and the two other women said that during totality, they had cried. The physicist couldn't believe it was over. He had been anticipating this event for years. He had tried to see a total eclipse once before, had traveled all the way to Paris for it, but clouds had obscured the sight. The others marveled that we were alive in the million or so year interval when the sun and the moon were the right size to create a corona. Once upon a time, the sun had been too small and the moon too large to see a ring of light. But now, the sun was expanding and the moon was moving away from us, making it appear to shrink. I ate my salad and tuna fish and listened to the others talk. I wondered why I hadn't cried. For dessert, we ate cantaloupe and, as I scooped it onto my plate, I confirmed that yes, the sun had been the color of melon. The banana bread was good despite being twice baked.

Later that afternoon, I called my boyfriend and told him the eclipse had been amazing. A few hours later, working at the restaurant, I smiled and nodded when my fellow servers gushed about the corona. How astounding, I agreed. Once in a lifetime. Going to the next one for sure. That eclipse was really something, huh? I said to my customers. The next day, I wrote to my family and friends about the eclipse, and I said at totality, I had felt *wonder*.

"Tell me more about that feeling," Kathleen said. Yes, what exactly did I mean by "wonder"? Wonder was what Dillard had felt at totality, when she felt like she was dead, when her world became a movie filmed in the Middle Ages, when everything felt lost. Wonder was what Kathleen felt in relationship with God, what she meant when she said that God offered her all the treasure and eternal joy, that the Holy Spirit warmed her soul and blessed her with infinite tenderness. Wonder was what kept her going when she felt like she was crawling in the darkness; wonder erased her doubt. Wonder was what Mary had felt when the angel Gabriel came to her and told her she would give birth to the Son of God, and she said yes with all their heart.

Wonder was not what I had felt during totality at all. I had not felt unusually alive. I had not traveled time. I had not been lost. I did not feel fear. I did not cry. Not once had I felt wonder during mass, in prayer, reading the Bible. I often felt bored, inadequate, and guilty. I was constantly doubting that God was real, and the doubt prevented me from surrender.

I said I felt wonder during the eclipse because I wanted to have experienced something profound. I wanted to be captivated. I didn't want to admit I was disappointed because I was worried what this said about me. Was I broken, insensitive to feeling, blind to beauty, permanently lost? I hid my feelings because I thought if I had not felt what Dillard had felt, what Kathleen felt, then there was a void within me. But if I don't admit my disappointment, if I'm not honest with myself, how can I make space to find what truly makes me feel wonder? Perhaps what I felt when Kathleen read aloud the Dillard piece was wonder—I was awed by how Dillard had pinned down her experience so precisely that I was transported four decades into the past, onto a hill I had never seen, awed by how she had transcended that individual experience, revealing its larger significance: Most of us are asleep to the truth that death can seize us at any time. The eclipse had, if only briefly, awakened her. Yes, our experiences of wonder may be quieter than an eclipse, than a glimpse of God, they may be contained within the pages of a book, but they are no less important. Let us recognize wonder when it comes, wherever from, however loud or large: a longing for something we don't understand. Let us pursue it, trusting that eventually, sometimes in slivers, sometimes in waves, sometimes after long silences, we will grasp more than we have before.

O Tired Love   it's easy to see the wire that connects

Brandon Jordan Brown

melody and mystery is short   How inspiration quickens
the   felted   hammers   in   the   formless   void
Let's   rename   the   beginning   of   recorded   history
The   First   Important   Piano   Poem   a   dirge   of   grace
pulled from between firmament and kelp   And I am a candle

on the glossy lid   my eyes closed while all your present houseguests
chatter   in   the   hallway   and   throw   bread   at   the   lake
O   look   at   you   being   virtuosic   at   everything   you   do
You've got my wax   my wick   thumbs heavy as bricks
and a tuning fork threading poise across the acres between your ears
Teeth like a row of grain silos   and a thick heel thudding

with   the   steadiness   of   a   metronome   Your   suspenders
are wide as closet doors!   At night   when daylight is
tucked up to its chin in exhaustion and quilts   strike
a match on your zipper   Take it to my head   even though I am only
worth my weight in wind   My best efforts unreasonably dim
The   slow   foxtrot   you   push   out

soft   and assembled by ear   as the bench creaks at its corners

lending weight to the song   O what is the chord that makes
creation   go   backwards   like   beautiful   scarves
sucked into a trunk   Is there another that causes the lid to close
And when will you know to play them   I'm only wondering
Are   you   able   to   dream   your   rehearsals   in   reverse

—<o>—

Epimetheus in the Shower

Megan Snyder-Camp

Like a Boss, his t-shirt said
before he gave it away. Gave fur

to squirrels, night vision to foxes. Gave away
everything: the marsh-reeds

drinking water, the radiant soil unbinding
metal from mica. The circular hearts of rabbits

the looking in of peacocks. The names themselves
glossy stones. Leaving us naked, emptyhanded, with only fire

and a machine like a loader
to shave it all down.

I used to shave him down
every week, running the oiled blade

across his turning head. I kept him neat.
His work scattered through the yard, bulbs

pressing up through cardboard boxes. If I had not forced you out here
whose would you be now. Your ex builds a balloon archway

in her yard with holiday colors. A regional skill
like terror, like folding. Kitty litter is what we need now

the school newsletter says, for the children when it isn't safe.
A few of us mail kitty litter to our senators. A regional movement,

a plate slipping over under. A tongue. I say one more year
you say over or under. We hunted them, my son says,

the Neanderthals are gone
because we hunted them.

—<o>—

Office Girl & University Hero, Chapter One: *Change*

Maya Jewell Zeller

(With some lines from Anne Carson, T.S. Eliot, Ghostbusters, & Stevie Nicks.)

Somehow Office Girl *made it to adolescence.*

There were stop signs on the way and red glimmering sharks and there were lamps lit only in the afternoon dark. There were loads of boring masses and laundry and things like place settings with multiple silverware. Office Girl dreamed of one day being a Real Person.

Office Girl continued toward adulthood.

Suddenly she was what she suspected might be a real person, working in an office, no less, with Chairs! And Fish Stamps! And Company Stationery! She liked to make piles of work and finish them that day. She loved the Inbox and the Outbox and she loved pulling the sticky notes from the edges of the computer screen and throwing them into the recycle bin. She liked to read trashy novels on her breaks; and at night, alone in her apartment, with the sky stitching up the day like a gash, she liked to read things like Anne Carson and Heraclitus and Ada Limón and Charles D'Ambrosio and Zell Fink. Or was it Nell Zink? She got them confused. They had so many Interesting Ideas! And Strange Shadows.

Then she met University Hero and all the shackles she didn't know confined her fell into heaps of writhing snakes. She met University Hero and was like, Well, Fuck!

Before this she rarely swore. She'd had a moment in first grade when she'd smacked her principal in the face, but other than that she mostly followed the rules, except for when she didn't. (Times she didn't: when the rules were in the way of her getting what she really wanted, when the rules seemed grossly inconvenient, when the rules went against her inner ethics, when the rules had poor rhythm, when the rules were written without thought to diction and concerns of imagistic fluency.) Her teacher had once told her she was headed for hell in a handbasket, which sounded quite charming. A tiny hell, in a basket of flowers? Lovely. Or a tiny hell, all mixed in with the rolls and muffins for the new neighbors! What would that be like? Burnt toast? Ha, ha—Office Girl laughed at her own joke. She went on to become head of her class.

Her aspirations were low, of course, as College Itself felt like a huge accomplishment. *Hooray for laurels!* said her relatives. But they didn't attend any of the ceremonies. Office Girl went on, as one might expect, to a well-paid Administrative Assistant 3 position.

Office Girl met University Hero when he was on his interview circuit. He happened to step in to ask where a particular office was—he was meeting the head of multimodal at ten—and when their eyes met they were *a pair of ragged claws scuttling/ across the floors of silent seas* and they were a pair of horses in a field, doing what wild horses do, perhaps galloping side by side and perhaps copulating and perhaps eating flies from one another's withers, and perhaps gazing intently into one another's furry/furrowed brows.

They recognized each other like Italics. The world poured back and forth between their eyes. Once. Or twice. As did the universe.

Where is the office of the multibrodal—ultimatefrisbeefcake— multiplescreens—catchersmittwellcuckoo—University Hero was having trouble forming speech, but somehow, Office Girl knew she could hear his thoughts. Indeed: already his scalp had begun to tingle. What disease might that be? He vowed to spend some time on WebMD. Tonight.

Floor three, Office Girl heard Office Girl say. But wouldn't you like to come with me to the roof instead–first? Your schedule says you have fifteen minutes, Office Girl heard Office Girl say. She reached into her secret key place. University Hero nodded. He muttered, exuberantly, those lines from that movie: *I am the gatekeeper./ I am the keymaster*. He chuckled. *This is going to be so fun. I'd been hoping for a portal to Authentic Adventure.*

The ladder to the roof was sixteen feet long, and each rung felt like a kind of ascension, or a sort of very advanced kegel, the kind when you can feel the rings of muscle in your vagina and you think wow this is like a tunnel ladder, and wow, spring coils, and holy shit vaginas really are quite strong, I'm so glad I started doing these exercises. Office Girl could feel University Hero behind her, and she knew, instinctively, that if she fell, he could catch her in his cape. This was maybe like the opposite of feeling you have a strong vagina or maybe it was similar in that things like feminism and all the other isms fell away for a moment and you were just two people who "Get It" together. She had never felt more afraid of falling, more alive, more afraid of not falling. She knew this was crazy. She thought of Leonard Cohen and she thought of Kurt Cobain and she thought of Stevie Nicks. She thought *I've been afraid of changing cause I/ built my world around you.*

But she knew those were the wrong lyrics in her case. Someone else out there needed them—someone afraid to make the change they needed to make their life right, to be more than merely content, to be real, to be transcendent. Sure, comfortable can happen even in a transcendent state, but that's not the same as mundanity. Or settling for something because of history and nice people. That sort of fear of changing. She, Office Girl, was not afraid of those changes. She was only afraid of not reaching the roof. Would they ever reach the roof? (His breathing behind her felt like a song. His breathing near her ankles made her feel stronger.) And then they did (reach the roof).

Somehow, though it was 9:52 a.m. and the sky had been bright outside her office window, the roof was dark and the firmament scattered with twinkling stars, mostly blue, some occasional yellow. Across them was written, as if in ink or blood or semen, or something less basic, maybe particulate mica mud on a rockface, *Office Girl, will you go to lunch with me?* It seemed a normal-ish request but given they'd only just met, during his interview circuit no doubt, it also seemed very forward (also there was the fact of it being scrawled there in the firmament, though University Hero stood next to her—how did he do that???). Yes, thought Office Girl. She'd read *Pride & Prejudice.* She thought, A thousand times yes! She could feel the whole castle shaking. Or maybe just the whole thousand acres of this campus. Or maybe she really did, wonderment on wonderment, understand the vibrations of the earth. Was she a seismograph? Was she a god?

It's time for your meeting with multimodal, she said aloud, and you need to go. But meet me in the coffeehouse on the corner of 8th and Walnut at noon, and I'll buy you a coffee. With cream. We'll see from there.

Between them flowed a current like the one that moves the ocean in its deepest crevasses, where the little fish with lights on their heads swim about, looking prehistoric, smelling like detritus. Between them flowed a current like the one that holds the moon to the earth, something gravitational, something forgiving and graceful and terrible and worthy. Holy shit, they both kept thinking. Is this happening for real? It was. (Though one of them may deny it later, for reasons of some sort of preservation.)

University Hero could hardly descend the ladder. He had been certain angels did not exist, and yet, here was one, glimmering shimmering and sparknet and clayhammock island and the catch of a treebranch filled with bursting blooms and pollen knees. Crashing through brush! A summit with yes!! *Yes,* he said to her, again and again. *Yes. Fuck Yes.* (He, too, was not accustomed to swearing. For her, he would have anything leave his mouth. He would have anything enter it. He wanted to unfold himself like a map, like a tulip, like a foal emerging from the birth sac. He wanted to push her off the roof and then swoop to save her. He wanted her to be the thing that made him dive to save her. He thought, This is simple. I'll just nail my interview.)

He had to nail this interview. It was imperative.

(He hummed Tina Turner to himself on his way to Multimodal. He was unfolding into his new name.)

—<o>—

this is the beneath

Savannah Slone

These are our eyes that can't blink.
These are our chipped teeth.

Our luminous, opal
buttonholes that we sew
together. Me, a marble ghost,
gazing into the mirror that isn't
there.

This is my sea of hips.
Ilium.   Ischium.   Pubis.
This is you, jangling my
pieces together like keys.

I sleep in a dissolving trundle
bed that doubles as an operating
table.   I am a self-surgeon.

        This is dissolving inaudible.

My tendons, even my cuticles, are recovery.

This body is a clinic.
This is a paper shredder
wherein we lay.

We, embers.
Them, tattered maps.
This is the prologue and
the epilogue.
                    This is our body.
Intramural plum cheekbone(s)
pillars holding me up.

—<o>—

Instruction Manual for Child

Shankar Narayan

	here is the a	
-lgorithm	here is the algo	
-rithm	scrape sandal paste from body	
	like Parvati make a war-	
rior	who would love her	this never
happened	no love	
	-manual for robots	your name
	is cub	you learn
like child	loop loop if then	remain you un
-configured		i am cruel to you
	just to see how you re-	
act	see if you break	an elephant
	always remembers	how light hits
	silicon windows	grows nose in elec-

tric lies   there are no real boys
glassmelt   is meta

-phor   so many potential   circuits
                              so many potential   differences

rhythm
-less   because orbits decay   loop loop

flatten   ellipsis   hum into me
your mother   -bot un-

separated   un
-separated   un-

separated   by cosmic distances   un
-separated   by   light-

years   tell you who
is alien   tell you who

to kill   force the boy
                              to break

its house   force the boy
to violence   some   -thing

the boy   is on his knees
the boy   is begging   you not

to force   him
to break   him

-self   let no one   disturb my ritual   only you

can see me   naked   every sandgrain
is a uni-   verse that   could turn

into a real boy   without warning
a real boy

but not too real
else i must be

-head   see the trident glittering
a smile   with three fangs

see the third eye
opening   with

-out   warning   with
-out   warning

you are warrior   re
-mover   of obstacles

kill
only as in   -structed

your name
is Ganesha

and are you   child
would you

be
you would   be

if only some-

one would raise you

like one

if only some

-one would love you

this never happened

—<o>—

Vacation

Stephanie Wong Ken

Mexico? her sister asked. Yes, Lena said. Land of sand and happy hour and ruins of the ancient Maya. They were warriors, right, or is that the Aztecs? her sister said. Either way, they sure didn't take any shit. Go get that sun. Her sister squeezed her shoulder, the good one, without any bruises yet to heal, the one free of his fingerprints. Might as well, she said to her sister. I'm wearing a bathing suit under this bathrobe, after all.

What was to be their one-week stay at ARCHITECTURAL MARVEL–TULUM, MX, becomes her one week stay alone. The rental property is managed by a young, gleeful looking guy from North Carolina named Roger. Shirtless locals carved out the modern kitchen and built the water-bed on the roof. She imagined Roger drawling against a background of jungle noise under the stars in the company of many, many women.

The Hidden World of the Maya, National Geographic: Cities of Blood, The Complete Mayan Gods. Going on a trip, Lena tells the librarian. She finds safety in knowing. But some men find her need to clarify insufferable. Put your pros and cons list away, he once told her, holding a pair of scissors the wrong way. It's insufferable.

The workmen stop talking to watch her unstick her legs from the seat and get out of the rental car to open the heavy wooden gate, the padlock slapping with the momentum. She can feel them honing in on the sweat line between her breasts and her bare thighs in a pair of white shorts. The stray dogs circle until she pulls into the driveway and then lower their tails and lose interest.

Do you want it fast or do you want it slow? The guy sitting next to her at the campus bar licked his lips and leaned in. Is that a joke? she asked. It's my best line, the guy said. Should I say it again?

Rodger from North Carolina is not waiting at sliding glass doors or by the small pool, grinning like she expected. Instead, he's left a bottle of complimentary rum and a typed note propped up on a glass table, the one he must leave all of his guests: *Howdee doo! Have the time of your life.*

Maybe it was cowardly, who knows when to talk about bones breaking. She told her sister she had a bad fall from a tree while drinking and slept all day in the guest room in a terry cloth bathrobe, under a cave of down comforters. Before she undressed to shower, she made sure the door was locked and when she moved around the kitchen or the yard, and she knew her sister was watching, she blamed it on aging hips, atmospheric shifts, their shared, pitiful genes.

I'm lounging in this cool, concrete house while Mexicans hang their laundry on clothesline between trees, she tells her sister on the phone. Awful, sure but don't kill the party before it even gets started, her sister says. It's all just one big ruin, Lena says. But it's great. I am disconnecting in five seconds.

The first night will be filed under: to be forgotten. After sitting in the pool in the square shade of the house until her finger pads became little deserts, she drinks the entire complimentary bottle of rum with ice from the bucket in the freezer. She ignores the giant plastic water jug with the awkward manual pump and the way the heat makes her face feel like gauze. Unsteady, but careful, she looks for a remote, a phone, anything. Small miracles, she thinks as she crash lands into the pool. Paradise.

He'd loved the still humidity on the body first thing in the morning, the cobalt tiles, the low-hanging fruit, the bats asleep in the trees. Mexico had been his choice—the ruins, the Maya. Because I love you, her sister says on the other end of the line, sounding very tired, I am going to ask you not to call back and to enjoy yourself. All right, she slurs, feeling dehydrated but also wet.

Some girls like a little bam bam, a slap or a good pull of the hair. Some girls are into bruising, bite marks, everywhere except the face. Which type are you? He was inside her, this person from a party she already wanted to forget. I don't know, she said, I don't know what type of girl I am.

At the turnstile to the ruins, someone issues a warning for iguanas and snakes. She stands in the afternoon heat and steadies herself against another wave of nausea, a metallic taste coating her tongue. She wants to the crawl back to the pool, back to the dream house behind the padlock.

Dear Distraught in Dawson's Creek, Dear Lonely in Lac-Lois, Dear Manic in Moose Jaw. Another night of advice for strangers required caffeine. She spotted him by the counter, holding the metal canister of cream. A boy from her high school in another city years ago. He ended up going to law school or teacher's college. Something solid after partying abroad in Laos and sleeping with the wrong housewife. He smiled at her, his hair flopping to one side the way she remembered it used to, guileless and non-threatening.

The tour guide, his face shadowed by a spotless white hat and half the agreed fee in his pants pocket, is eager to tell her about the watchtowers, the famous ball court, and the temple you can climb, unassisted. The hat makes him stand out from the other guides in their clean shirts and leather shoes, huddled under the shade of a twisted Ficus tree behind the BIENVENDOS sign, calling out tour, 300 pesos, four for 400. Welcome, the guide says to Lena, holding a binder between his palms. American? He smiles, polite. His face is a grid of thin lines curving around his eyes and mouth. Canadian, she says. Though she could just as easily have said, Not from here.

The worst person she ever dated? The alcoholic, she told him on their tenth date, when dates are really eating between sleeping and then sleeping together. We met during my last year of university. He would barge into my apartment at four am, completely loaded, and try to get me to wake up so we could go to an after hours club or some karaoke bar. Once, he stumbled in and pissed all over my laptop. That's disgusting, her date said, laughing. Oh, I know, she said.

Next to the watchtower of stone, the guide runs his fingers on a laminated drawing of a large tree with enough branches for thirteen gods, and a net-work of roots stretching deep underground to represent the world of the dead. A group of French school children sit nearby in a pile, waiting for their guide to also explain the tree. Lena studied the names in the creased library book, but there are so many, it's hard to keep them straight. Who is your favorite god? she asks her guide. I like the Cipactli, he says, touching his hat. *El cocodrilo*. The Earth Monster with the world on his back.

I just drank a lot of cough syrup and watched movies alone, he told her behind a flop of dirty hair when she asked him why he never went out in high school. Once, he drank too much Robitussin and believed he was seeing his body in his bedroom from above and could tell there was some kind of growth, like a tree stump, coming out of the top of his head. So he tried to remove it with his fingers. I cleaned up after that, he said. Often, she'd wake up to him touching the scar in his sleep.

Pourquoi il y a tant de dieux? a French school child asks the schoolteacher, who then asks their guide in broken English. Lena stops taking pictures of the iguanas to listen to his answer. That is like asking why there are so many clouds in the sky, the guide says, shaking his head at the teacher and the child.

He was skeptical of vacations, of taking time away from your life to enjoy yourself. She begged him to book the trip anyway. A year into their relationship and some of their friends were already married, already pregnant, already drying orchid leis in the creases of their photo albums.

The gods made beings from yellow and white maize, her guide explains. When the sun rose on the first day, the humans were flesh. They had brains, recognized their creators, and worshipped them, but the gods thought they had too much knowledge. So they clouded their eyes to keep them focused on day-to-day events. But not too clouded, of course. Her guide smiles at her, at his joke.

Sometimes, they would have to red flag certain letters. Someone came up with a pitying name for them: the cry for help letters. Read them once, then notify the supervisor. Someone else would try to reach the person and provide a number for a helpline or the police. At the time, Lena had not felt qualified enough to write back.

A Danish couple wanders up to her guide, crashes her tour. Is it all right? the girl asks her, handing her a few hundred pesos, clearly stoned. Her boyfriend also looks pretty moony, resting his dirty fingernails in the dip of the girl's back.

The copper pipes in the show home had already been stripped, along with the door knobs and the door pegs. Wind and a small fire had erased most of the evidence of someone squatting there. She thought they were playing around, looking for a room with good light for fucking. He said, hold still, Lena, positioning her against a wall. He punched the wall, letting chunks of plaster float in the air, forming a circle of holes around her body. When he finished, she turned to stare. She watched a trail of spit fall from his mouth.

The guide cycles like a pro, balancing his binder on the handlebars of a small yellow three speed. She can barely keep up. The bruises on her shoulder and ribs are burning. The Danish couple cycle behind her, laughing. Tourists in bike taxis gaze at the patchy forest along the path. She can tell which ones are beginning their tours and which ones are reaching the end, sun-dazed despite their sunglasses, their drivers talking louder, grinning harder to earn a good tip in the last available mile. She feels the flash and realizes the Danish boyfriend has aimed his camera at her. Hey, she yells, turning to look at him, to leer. But he is speeding up, holding his camera high in one hand to get shots of the forest and the tops of people's heads, making peace signs at everyone he passes.

In a video chat with her editor, she tried to explain why she felt comfortable answering this particular letter. There are drawings in crayon, for God's sake, she said. Okay but I think the mother figure is holding something sharp? And is that blood pouring down or rain? her editor said, holding the kid's stick figures very close to his large, sweaty face. I think it may be best to pass on this one, her editor said, already moving on.

In bushes by the pathway, she vomits. Here, the Danish girl says, handing her a bottle of water. The rum, Lena thinks as she retches into the dirt, holding her ribs with her arms. Her sister warned her, as she always does. This is very nice, the girl says, looking at the landscape. But it's no Thailand. Shit, she yells, jumping back. There are snakes.

I'm apologizing to you. Lena? He was on his knees, showing her despair, the S-shaped scar on the top of his head.

The ball court is impressive; two slanted walls of stone angled to form a triangular court the size of a football field. A metal ring is still intact on one of the walls, jutting out from a spot that looked impossible to access, at least from where they are on the ground. What about all those human sacrifices? the boyfriend asks, leaning his elbows against his girlfriend. Oh no, the guide says, standing with his hands folded next to the stone tablet of a god. Only blood sacrifice for this game.

That night, she drove slow because she is night blind. Another search through alleyways and the familiar bars. Her sister was calling but she couldn't move one side of her body, the side closest to the phone. That was her excuse. Squinting in the dark of the car window, she thought, is that him or a dog or a dead deer in the road?

The steps look like death traps, tiny, uneven pads on the face of the 138-foot temple. Ixmoja, the tallest temple pyramid on the Yucatán peninsula, the guide tells them, Reach the top, make a wish. The French kids climb ahead, slipping on the stone steps in their polished shoes, reaching their sweaty palms out for guardrails and safety ropes that are not there. The Danish couple stop every few steps to take pictures of the view. Lena has visions of falling school children, their terrified faces caught mid frame.

It wasn't rain, it was blood, and now she would have to get back in the car and drive with the high beams on to see through it and find some road that went away from his body, lying in the middle of the turning lane. A straight line, across an ocean.

At the top of the temple, they wave down at the guide, sitting on a rock under a tree, the white hat resting in his hands. *The Cipactli*, she thinks as she leans in to pose with the couple. *The world balancing on her back*. She forgets about her shoulder, her arm, and her ribs, so instead of smiling, she is grimacing. Shielding the sun from her eyes, she stares at the vastness of the ruins. The small details, she is sure, will be important later.

—<o>—

Alchemy

Chelsea Dingman

The clover, cross-eyed in a field of witch
grass, grows bald in the wind

amid the shatter of small children
& I'm tired, again, of pretending

kind men exist somewhere. As a child,
men were suns at the glass, the fires

that result. Dear god, you must be a torch
among them, setting the fields aflame

inside my own heart. Last night,
the wolfish wind leapt. The trees shook.

The stars died a little quicker. A man
called me names I disavowed when I

accepted I was human. Oh humanity:
what is more overrated than the human

heart? Confound me. I am speaking
for the clover. The grass. The green bosom

of field I long to love as the wind loves
the future woman I have yet to—

Something Must be Done!

Matt Greene

I remember the one they called the Big One. I was apartment hunting at the time, seeing a unit in Greenwood. It was ugly—teal carpet, plastic bookshelf, but there was this old, wooden arm chair that I liked. I remember trying it out and running my fin over a lion carved into one of the armrests.

"Does it come with the unit?" I asked the landlady.

"You betcha!" she said.

She had metallic bluish scales and a beehive hairdo. I was thinking that if I didn't get the apartment, maybe I could get a date.

Of the old gang, I was the longest to hold on, but now I too needed a place of my own. At first there'd been a gaggle of us aspiring types, Alan and Nathan and Susie and Drew and Tina and Tammi, a couple Jeffs. We rented an old house and waited tables, landscaped part-time, made latte foam art. We watched Romanian New Wave films and read our sound poems to one another. Rent was split equally, which is to say nobody paid.

But then, as if overnight, we got older. Jeff and Tammi and Jeff and Tina shacked up and wanted to procreate and buy new houses with fenced off enclosures to keep their young from escaping. So it went. Everyone got a job with a tech company or they ran away to the edge of civilization, or both. Soon enough I was the only sockeye left in that big house, just me and my *ideals*.

One day, I was watching a Dziga Vertov film and smoking French cigarettes when a notice was stapled to my front door. It said the building was going to be leveled to make way for condos.

"Hey," I asked the Greenwood landlady, admiring her red velvet mumu and muscular pectoral fins, "Is there any way a guy like me, with no credit and a part-time job, might skip to the top of the application pile?"

She started wiggling her tail. Only it was less a wiggle than a vibration. Her fins sort of swiveled around. I'd never seen anything like it but I felt the situation demanded a response, so I tried doing it too, this mating dance, if that's what it was. Only it wasn't that at all, it was the earthquake getting started.

"What's going on!?" the landlady shouted. She pressed her fins against her beehive hairdo to keep it in place.

"What do you *want* to be going on?" I asked back, having somehow not yet realized the magnitude of what was happening.

She reached out and touched my fin, then pushed me aside and hurried to a door frame. I crouched under a table. There was a cracking sound like a roar and out the window I could see trees ripped in half right up the middle. Buildings tumbled over like dominos. The whole apartment building crumbled around us and everything was pulverized, save her door frame, my table, and the old arm chair.

It occurred to me that the landlady and I might be the last two salmon alive.

"I can't believe your hair is still perfect," I said.

Only she didn't hear what I'd said because a chasm had ripped open and we were hurtled away from each other.

"What?" she cried out.

"I said, 'your hair is still perfect!'"

Magma oozed in cute patterns: a fern, a heart, the Amazon logo. I saw brunch spots, charcuteries, and tapas bars swallowed by earth.

Since the unit I'd come to see had been ripped apart, I immediately resumed apartment hunting. There was no time to lose! Too often they give the place to the first schmo who shows up. In fact the Greenwood apartment was the fourth place I'd seen that day.

The Smith Tower had been knocked sideways by the quake, coming to rest at a 45 degree angle against a pile of rubble. Seeing that the building looked abandoned, I took up residence in the penthouse.

The place needed redecorating so I started pilfering furniture: a couch from this condo, a laptop from an abandoned houseboat. I even returned to the wreckage of the Greenwood apartment to collect the old armchair, which, as it turned out, was some kind of antique. According to a plaque on the chair, it was a gift given in 1914 by the last Empress of China, Cixi, to the mayor of Seattle. It took a while to bolt everything down so it wouldn't slide across the hardwood to the ground-facing windows, and even longer to get used to the pull of gravity as I cooked up breakfast, took a sideways shower.

Word got out about my new digs and, by the weekend, everyone wanted to see me. I threw a big party. The Jeffs and Tammi and Tina even drove in from the suburbs.

"Poetry is the ecstatic rendered into static," I said.

"Property is the illusion of time as capital," I said.

Everyone applauded. We toasted cocktails with fennel vinegar to celebrate Tina's new self-composting toilet, Tammi's new job in HR, Nathan's new haberdashery.

The next day I saw some other salmon come sniffing around the place, so I went out on the balcony and shouted, "Hey you! Yeah you! Scram! These are *my* digs!"

Others came by from time to mine. If hollering wasn't enough, I'd slap my fins against my chest, or throw some garbage at them, or recite sections of the manifesto I wrote in college for a course on sustainable urban planning… *Lichen for every rooftop! Kombucha mothers for every closet! Recalibrate root chakra from consume/decay to ferment/foment! We ARE the automaton!*

Weeks passed, and my parties became a big deal. Every Friday night we'd dangle from ropes to keep from falling and drink and talk, looking down at the rubble below. But, at the end of the night, after the guests had left, there I would be, holding onto a support rope, all alone.

One day I saw the landlady wiggling her tail fin below my window. "Yoohoo!" she said.

I ignored her and returned my attention to my crossword puzzle and bagel.

"Yoohoo-oo!" she said.

When I let her in, she said she wanted me to rent her a place in the tower. As the only occupant, I guess I was the de-facto landlord.

"How's your credit?" I asked.

She touched my fin.

"OK, OK you can move in!" I blurted.

Her name was Shirley. We both loved Don Quixote and vaping CBD weed. She was a poet, and when she read to me I would become lost in her voice… *"I met a fella in the reefs/Full caudal finned—a sprite most fair/His lateral line was long, his operculum was light/I even awed his nares."*

Shirley was good with a hammer. She went about fixing up the place, making new floors that were flat instead of slanted, filling in all the cracks in the walls.

Life was good. Sometimes I did get anxious and think about all the folks who had occupied the building before the quake, but why was the Smith Tower any more theirs than mine? *Predatory capitalism?* Typewriter and firearm magnate Lyman Cornelius Smith died before the construction of his tower had finished. I did hope all the old occupants weren't dead, but I had no intention of giving up my penthouse.

Our days were leisurely. Shirley would write for a few hours while I diddled around in the kitchen, experimenting. I made all kinds of things with my abundant free time, Taiwanese plankton omelets, plankton mofongo, planklax cured with brandy and dill. After meals we'd stroll the avenues, or what was left of them, and talk about capital-A Art.

"BOMB Magazine has gone all corporate," Shirley said one night.

"I know," I said, "Tell me about it."

I reached for her fin, and she squeezed.

But, as the weeks passed, Shirley grew distant. My affection grew and grew, but I wasn't sure the feeling was mutual. Some nights she spent hours drifting around the penthouse as if in a fugue state. I hoped it was a poet thing.

"What's wrong?" I asked her one night. She'd been gazing out at the landscape beyond the windows for fifteen minutes.

"Don't you worry about them?" she said. "All those people out there."

"Sort of," I said, and then realized that wasn't a very nice thing to say. It was true that not everyone was doing well after the quake. Some had no choice but to live in tents or caves.

"Something must be done!" I said.

We invited over my old pal Alan, who had also done quite well for himself. He'd taken up residence in the Kingdome and ate all the hot dogs and nachos he wanted. Alan and I put up flyers all over town, on telephone poles and coffee shop bulletin boards, in the windows of patisseries and brewpubs. We took out a full-page ad in the local weekly. It said, quite simply: "SOMETHING MUST BE DONE!"

We held our meeting in the Kingdome on the turf of the playing field. Almost everyone in town had turned up, even Susie and Nathan and both Jeffs and Tammi and Tina. In the spirit of camaraderie and togetherness, we sat in a large circle, seminar-style, and Alan facilitated the discussion. A redistribution of wealth was settled on, with, of course, a few exceptions. For example, the Jeffs and Tammi and Tina didn't want to give up their nice new houses and I quite liked my penthouse. But I gave up all the other floors, on the condition I was made emperor, which, we all thought, seemed fair given that I had organized the meeting. All food resources were shared from then on. Some fished for plankton while others farmed zucchinis and kale or foraged berries. Others scrapped the rubble. We scavenged steel, which we used to make pedestrian bridges. Only it didn't go so well. I picked the most elaborate, impractical designs and they turned out so flimsy that they'd crumble under the weight of a single pedestrian.

Shirley had a way of finding new problems.

"I thought you should know," she said. "No one can find parking in Greenwood anymore."

"Oh boy," I said.

I imagined a great parking structure that rose to the heavens, and then remembered our flimsy pedestrian bridges. I was a lousy emperor.

Shirley left to go read. She'd been working through Proust. I wish I could I say I never had the patience for it, but I never even picked up the books. Shirley had thought we might read them together, but I told her it was baseball season.

Lapping back and forth across the living room, I looked from the lamp to the table as if they might divine what needed to be done. Trying to clear my head, I took a seat in my old armchair and felt a terrible shaking. Another earthquake, and this one was even worse than the last!

Or maybe I'm remembering it all wrong. Maybe the Big One didn't hit at all until I lived in the Smith Tower, and the first was just an ordinary earthquake. Either way, my whole life crumbled in front of my eyes. I clung to a banister and felt that I was falling, that the whole building was resuming its journey from vertical to horizontal. When it was over, I found myself engulfed in a cloud of Smith Tower dust.

I set off with urgency to find Shirley, swimming through the rubble as fast as I could. I surfaced just in time to see Shirley dragged away by a pair of plate-armored geoducks.

"Where are you taking Shirley?!" I cried.

The geoducks took over the whole city, just like that. They'd been planning for eons, waiting for the right moment and now that the quake had freed them of the muck at the bottom of the Sound, the geoducks grew tall and strong, sprouted many limbs with which they grasped spears, shields, and pistols.

My empire lay in tatters and many of my fellow Seattleites had been taken as prisoners of war, destined for the work camps or the coal mines.

For days I scrounged for crusts of bread and slept in parks where fallen trees formed natural shelters. I never stayed in one place for more than a night. Alone, shivering, I'd hear a noise and hold my breath, unsure if the wind had shifted or a geoduck approached.

Soon enough, I was discovered, not by a geoduck but by Tina.

"Well, hello, stranger," she said.

Tina was organizing a rebellion in shadows, joining together the urbanites with the fascists of the distant suburbs, who, I've neglected to mention, had established their own far bleaker society in the days after the first quake. If there was one thing we could all agree on, it was that we hated geoducks.

"I can almost taste it," Dirk said. Dirk was the leader of the fascists, a Chinook with throbbing muscles sculpted by years of the paleo diet. "Grilled geoduck. Geoduck sashimi. Geoduck linguini."

"In squid ink sauce!" I chimed in.

"Shut up!" Dirk said.

Tina patted my shoulder. "There, there," she said.

I had to admit, they cut a fearsome duo, the two of them.

Dirk and Tina trained us for weeks at a makeshift camp, near Marysville, due east of the Walmart on 64th. In a grassy clearing surrounded by green belt, we learned to army crawl, to slit a geoduck's umbo off clean, not to fire until we saw the whites of their shells. We ate nothing but hemp protein powder, slept for no more than two hours each night.

"We will prevail!" Dirk and Tina chanted.

"We will prevail!" we chanted back.

One night the wind blew open Dirk's tent flap and I caught a flash of the two of them making out... but that's neither here nor there.

The time came and we made our attack.

The geoducks had built a seemingly impenetrable cube-city in the old Pioneer Square, a three hundred-story superstructure where they all lived. Other land was devoted to agriculture or plundered for natural resources. The great forests of the North Cascades had been totally decimated—turned into bookshelves the geoducks sold to a foreign furniture company.

Assault rifles strapped to our backs, we rode BMX bikes from our camp to I-5 and hid under the overpasses, waiting for geoduck patrols to pass. On arriving in the city, we stopped at Discovery Park to rest, and Dirk and Tina brought out bottles of Syrah to enliven our spirits. We raised our glasses.

"Lock and load!" Tina said.

The plan was for some of us to head due east and then make camp on the top of Beacon Hill. When the time came, we would set out for the Cube just as the others rushed down from Discovery Park.

Only we never made it there. As we slurped the last of the wine, geoducks came at us on all sides.

Dirk fired round after round, crying, "Ahhhhhh!"

A spear shot through his midsection, and he fell to the ground. All around us, they slashed off fins and slit our gills. We were no match for the geoducks. I felt a blow at the back of my head and thought I was done for.

I came to in a prison cell. A single dull light bulb flickered on and off. I figured I must have been somewhere in the innards of the Cube. Soon, I heard someone approaching. The slot at the bottom of my cell door swung open, and there appeared the collected volumes of "In Search of Lost Time." I picked up "Swann's Way" and felt butterflies.

"Shirley!" I cried.

"Ssssssh," she said. "Not so loud."

I wanted so badly to see her face.

"Open the door," I said.

"That's not possible," she said.

"But—"

"Don't ask too many questions. You wouldn't like the answers."

"Shirley!" I cried.

"Just know I'm doing all I can," she said.

Her visits were infrequent, without pattern. Always she wanted to hear my progress with Proust, but, even in that horrible cell, I couldn't muster the patience. I tried to lie my way through conversations.

"I just got to the part where they go bowling," I said.

"Bowling?"

"With bumpers."

Shirley told me all about the geoducks' lives inside the Cube. They didn't go out much. They'd get up, drink a Rockstar and go to work (they were mostly programmers and engineers), then they'd commute up or down the Cube back to their housing unit, where they'd microwave a Hot Pocket for dinner and pass the night playing computer games and chatting with each other on something called Reddit. It disgusted me.

But not Shirley.

"How would you like to live in the muck? For generations?" she said.

"I thought they liked it there."

"I've learned their language," she said. "They speak in code. C++."

I imagined them stomping around hallways, self-important erections in diaper shells.

"Good for you," I said.

"I told you I'm doing all I can."

"Oh," I said. "Great."

When Shirley next visited, it was to tell me there was someone else.

"All because I can't stand Proust," I said.

"Of course you think it's all about you," she said.

"How did you meet him?"

"Mortimer was my minder in the labor camp. Our first date was at the Red Robin on the 264th floor."

"Why do they keep me here?" I asked.

"They don't think you're fit for the mines," she said.

"And you? Why have they spared you from the mines?"

"I swore allegiance to the geoduck way."

I was speechless. In fact, I took a vow of silence. I went on a hunger strike.

Shirley next visited with Mortimer. When I saw them entering my cell, side by side, I had to admit he was a handsome geoduck. Certainly better looking than I.

He said he could arrange for me to swear allegiance.

"Never!" I shouted, and then blushed because I had accidentally broken my vow of silence.

The punishment for refusal was execution.

Guards dragged me into an ornate chamber filled with the skeletal remains of other salmon. A small crowd had gathered. Most had snacks—popcorn, tortilla chips, soda. Shirley and Morty sat next to each other. They at least they had the decency not to eat.

I was put in a stiff chair—my old antique chair. My fins were cuffed to the armrests and I was gagged.

The death squad raised their spears and pistols. Shirley broke out sobbing.

The chamber doors flew open and Tina appeared, guns blazing, with the forces of the rebellion behind her.

"Eat lead!" she cried.

Dirk charged in, too, a knife in each fin. Somehow he must have survived.

"Sashimi-time," Dirk said, spitting in various directions.

Or maybe *that* was when the Big One hit, right after they'd put me in the chair and the cavalry arrived. I remember everyone sort of stumbling around, not sure if they should still be fighting. But, come to think of it, maybe it was all one long earthquake, maybe we'd been shaking the whole time... regardless, their city was swallowed by the depths not a moment after I slipped out the backdoor.

The quake pushed Seattle up on a tectonic ridge where it drained of water. On Yesler Way Orcas flopped from side to side. A giant squid slapped anything and everything in reach with his enormous tentacles, and Dirk got stuck to a suction cup. I watched in horror as the squid pulled Dirk into its mouth, chewed once with a loud crunch, and swallowed.

From wide seismic fissures, I saw emerge figures the horrors of which the surface world had never seen. Their gnarled appendages sprouted into five digit clumps, two of which had opposable thumbs. They had reeking belly buttons holes. And their ears! Gross!

Before I could ask these monsters what they were called, I was pulled away by the riptide of a seismic tidal wave. I waved goodbye to Seattle for good, and hello to a passing humpback whale, which sang its greeting back at me. I had no idea what she was saying.

—<o>—

A Conversation with Mattilda Bernstein Sycamore

Interviewed by Alex Davis-Lawrence, February 2019

Mattilda Bernstein Sycamore is a prolific and powerful writer, editor, and activist. Her latest novel, *Sketchtasy*, was chosen by NPR as one of the Best Books of 2018, and is a finalist for a 2019 Lambda Literary Award—an honor her memoir, *The End of San Francisco*, won in 2013. Other books include the novels *So Many Ways to Sleep Badly* (2008) and *Pulling Taffy* (2003), and the anthology *Why Are Faggots So Afraid of Faggots?* (2012), which was an American Library Association Stonewall Honor Book. She has edited four additional non-fiction anthologies, including *Nobody Passes: Rejecting the Rules of Gender and Conformity* (2007) and *That's Revolting! Queer Strategies for Resisting Assimilation* (2004), and spent ten years as the reviews editor for *Make/shift*. She now lives in Seattle.

Interviewer

You've just wrapped up your tour for *Sketchtasy*, and you're back in Seattle. What was the experience of the tour like for you?

Sycamore

The tour was pretty amazing. The experience has really given me energy to continue being in the world. As you know, I did the tour over a long period of time, and I was away from Seattle in total for nine months. I did the east coast first, then the west coast. Every event was different, but what I've been thinking of since I've finished the tour is the energy that I feel in a room, where the audience is really connecting with me and my work. There's a direct engagement, and a deep intimacy, and a camaraderie, and a sense of creating a history together. I keep thinking—how do I bring that into my life every day?

Interviewer

I definitely felt that energy at the reading I attended. In terms of the sense of history you're talking about, I found it interesting to think about the different generations of people who are part of this community... people who are looking at *Sketchtasy* having been there, or at least been cognizant of that scene and culture as it was happening—as well as people who are looking back on it as history.

Sycamore

One thing that was interesting and that I didn't expect in writing the book, in writing about this particular place and time—Boston in 1995—is that in some ways it became a generational story. This is a generation of queens and queers who have grown up with AIDS diffusing their desires, and no way to imagine anything else. The characters mostly are in their late teens, early 20s. They're not the generation of queers who grew up, and then experienced sexual liberation, and then everything fell apart, and people lost their entire circles of friends... they just had to cross everyone out of their datebook because they were all dead. It's not that generation; it's a generation that grew up not being able to imagine anything else. And this generation isn't really talked about as much. We hear about the previous generation, and we hear about a generation after, where there are medications that make HIV into a manageable condition for many, and that's the generation that started just after the time of the book.

I do think there was a generational pull, and what you're saying about people who lived through this period, and people who didn't but who also feel a kind of connection to it—I find that very exciting.

I think that I'm writing against nostalgia. Nostalgia, to me, is a longing for something that never happened. It's a glossy consumer product that replaces the nuance and the messiness of the lived experience. One thing I think that people are responding to about *Sketchtasy* is that the nuance and the lived experience and the messiness are there—and that feels exciting, and validating.

Interviewer

I was reading another interview that you gave, and you said something that's stuck with me: "the opposite of nostalgia is truth, so that's what I'm reaching for with this book." One of the things that really jumped out at me about your work is that you almost have the sensibility of a historian. The experiences that you're capturing and recounting would not be accessible without your writing. And to access that history in a way that provides context, and understanding, and truth—instead of this kind of nostalgic fabrication—might otherwise be impossible.

That ties in to an element of the book that stood out to me, which is how art, music, movies, and books are such an essential part of how Alexa accesses her emotions, identity, and sense of history. At the reading, you described the movies as "something that she used to find kinship with the generation that came before." What makes art such an important tool for Alexa, and for people in general, as a way to understand their own lives?

Sycamore

I think Alexa—living in Boston, a city rabidly afraid of difference, in a gay culture that mimics some of the worst aspects of straight hypocrisy—just walking around, she's constantly attacked, and this was true of all the characters in the book, more or less. In order to survive, Alexa has to be critically engaging at all times, and also has to broadcast a kind of toughness. There is a shutting off that is required in that daily experience of surviving brutality. And I think one of the things that happens for her in reading books is that they allow her to have her own emotional response to what's happening to her, in a way that she can't otherwise. Ordinarily, she has to keep those responses in, in order to survive. There are two books that are particularly meaningful to her, one of which is Rebecca Brown's *The Gifts of the Body*, which had just come out when Alexa reads it, in 1995. It's about a caretaker taking care of people dying of AIDS—in reading that, there's a kind of intergenerational kinship that is not possible in her own life.

This is an open question in a certain way, about queer worlds in general… I don't think there is much of an intergenerational kinship in the world, and part of that of course is due to AIDS and how many people died, but part of it is also due to the kind of segmenting and ageism of the gay culture that exists in the book, which is still the same gay culture that exists now, if not worse, where it's racist, and homophobic, misogynist, classist, ableist, transphobic, you know, go down the list… that culture doesn't allow kinship of any sort. There is this unopened question about what is intergenerational kinship, and is it possible?

Interviewer

What can we do to be better at maintaining and building that sense of intergenerational community moving forward—to start bridging these gaps that you're describing?

Sycamore

I'll talk about that on a few levels. On one level, on an intimate level, a personal level, the thing that I always think is missing is accountability.

If we build accountability in our own social circles, in our own artistic endeavors, in our own creative life, in our own communities, then that's what actually opens up the possibility for any kind of honest connection. On a larger, structural level, the so-called gay or LGBT or LGBTQ movement is always priortizing the people with the most privilege—and I think what needs to happen is always prioritizing the people who are the most marginalized.

The first scene in the book maps this trend, in a sense… I think 1995 does mark the moment when the assimilationist trajectory of gay politics took over. Before that, for decades, there was a struggle between a liberationist ethic which said, 'we need to end dominant institutions of oppression,' and assimilationist ideology, which said, 'we need to become part of those institutions of oppression.' Somewhere around 1995 marks the triumph of the assimilationists. Of that pull. In gay, and LGBT, and even queer politics in many ways, I think we've never recovered from that. Anything that challenges that stranglehold, and opens up the possibilities for accountability and mutuality and self determination, is something that moves us towards communal possibility, and communication across all the different boundaries of identity that could pull us together, but often set us apart, because of the way that the hierarchies of dominant hypocritical straight culture are magnified in some ways in countercultures, or subcultures, or allegedly oppositional cultures.

Interviewer

Absolutely. My feeling (and I was very young at that time, so this is a case of looking back) is that a lot of what was happening in that moment was driven by capitalism… you talk in *Sketchtasy* about the 'Uncommon Clout' Visa card—the credit card that sold itself on the claim that some of its profits would be given back to the gay community—and you can draw kind of a direct thread from that up through Budweiser sponsoring the pride parade, up through the ostensible progressiveness of Silicon Valley…

a sentiment that's just clearly absurd on its face. That was happening in the 90s in a lot of different areas, this transformation of a subculture into, basically, a demographic. When businesses realize that this community is a demographic they can define, and profit from, and reach into, it starts to shape and reward all the worst sides of that community.

When I'm looking at the political moment right now, I keep finding myself face to face with this type of person who's ostensibly very progressive, but is essentially just performing this kind of capitalist leftism that ultimately exacerbates the very problems they're ostensibly fighting. I think this is something that you speak to frequently, and that's a recurring theme in your work—as with the father in *The End of San Francisco* with his 'Stop Family Violence' stamp, or the opening scene with the fight over the AIDS ribbon in *Sketchtasy*.

Sycamore

Yeah, the scene that opens *Sketchtasy* is, Alexa is in a cafe, and basically, she's just ranting about the meaninglessness of the red ribbon, as an emblem of straight pity for people dying of AIDS. It's straight people leveraging their pity in order to gain political clout, and she's like, "it's just an empty symbol," and then someone just starts screaming at her, another queer youth, and allegedly it's about the red ribbon, but it just ends up being 'you don't deserve to live,' essentially. And this is someone who perhaps does not have privilege, but is acting like the people who do, and has internalized that kind of ideology.

You mentioned the Uncommon Clout Visa card, 'the card that gives back to the gay community, ten cents at a time'—those kind of gestures were relatively new in the 90s, the early to mid 90s, and to see in the intervening 25 years… I mean now, things that I would only have imagined as the most absurd satirical skit, you know, like trans military inclusion… no one would have talked about that 10 years ago, it would just be unimaginable. And that whole so-called issue just emerged because one person, considered the first trans billionaire, Jennifer Pritzker, who is an heir to the robber baron fortune of the Pritzkers of Chicago, donated $1.35 million to this institute called the Palm Center for this particular issue. Then, boom, it's a centerpiece of the LGBT agenda. So if you ever want to know how much it costs to get your issue at the center of a so-called national movement, it's $1.35 million, and that's really cheap. In comparison to national politics in general, that's awfully cheap. Now we see things, like an article saying, 'isn't this amazing, we now have non-binary and genderqueer fashion models,' and I'm like, 'No, what would be amazing is the end of the fashion industry!'

When you become part of an oppressive system—the fashion industry, the military-industrial complex—you know, you make it stronger, and it is frightening that people don't stop to actually think about how participating in dominant institutions of oppression furthers oppression, and instead choose to see that as the ultimate sign of success, or progress. I think that narrative is so misguided.

Interviewer

Right… if the goal is just to have more people, or a more diverse group of people, occupying the top of this oppressive structure, it doesn't actually change the structure in any way. It just changes which particular individuals are on top. Your piece in the *Baffler* about trans inclusion in the military was really powerful, and what you're saying is so obvious when you say it out loud, but it's just not part of the dialogue. It's very frustrating.

I wanted to shift the conversation—though I think, of course, all this stuff is connected in certain ways—back to Seattle and to the new book you're working on, *The Freezer Door*, which Semiotext(e) is publishing in Fall 2020. I was wondering if you could talk about that project a bit.

Sycamore

I'm calling *The Freezer Door* a lyric essay, because it circles around this question of desire and impossibility. And through that lens it's about gentrification, it's about the hypocritical allure of gay male sexual culture, it's about the dream of queerness, it's about Seattle very specifically, it's about the white picket fence in the eyes—that tech mentality, of a gated worldview, even when you don't have the gates—it's about the triumph of the suburban imagination over city life, and it's about this dream of a city as a place where you meet everyone and everything that you never imagined, and whether that dream can still exist in our homogenized cities of today. It's in a very elliptical style, where I'm circling around my own experience in Seattle of being in public space, being in the world, and trying to find sex and love and intimacy on my own terms and being stifled, through a variety of tragic encounters.

Interviewer

What you just described brings to mind something Alexa says in *Sketchtasy*, which I was going to bring up earlier: "There's a lot I'll do for tricks—role play, fantasies, whatever—but I'm not going to say I love you. That's just demeaning." There's this way in which love and intimacy, especially in this age of tech and social media and dating apps and so on, has also really become part of this momentum we've been talking about, this hungry thing, this system that's hungry for anything real that can be converted into new demographics and profit. How can we keep love and intimacy protected from that?

Sycamore

I like that you bring up that part in *Sketchtasy*, because Alexa, in turning tricks, in the whole book really, she's trying to create her own value system and her own morality that isn't perhaps what one would generally expect. And sometimes she succeeds and sometimes she fails, but in this particular moment, she has this trick who just keeps saying "say that you love me, say it." And Alexa doesn't see sex work as demeaning—that's what the dominant culture would say, dominant straight or gay culture—but what is demeaning is that people ask you to lie. And it's a lie about something that actually matters.

In *Sketchtasy* there is that question of how can love and intimacy be created, and I think in the book, drugs are the way that community is formed. And we know, any reader knows, the limitations of that, but there are also possibilities—drugs and going out and dancing and club culture are how these characters are able to actualize themselves in certain ways. And some of them, they're the standard self-hating gay men until they take that potion, and then everything changes. Alexa is living inside that hypocrisy, but club culture is also a way of living outside of a certain kind of normalcy. These are characters that don't live in the 9-to-5 world, they live in the 9 pm to 5 am world. The less they interact with broader culture, the better.

I think the question in *The Freezer Door*… it's a similar question but it's also a different one. First off, *Freezer Door* is nonfiction, and is very specifically about my life. It may be a central question in my life. The dreams that I want to have, of queer worlds that simultaneously challenge the violence of the status quo and build vivid and dynamic alternatives… I believe in that dream, but I don't see it in the world. I just see more hypocrisy. And at this point, that hypocrisy in queer worlds is way more damaging to me than the standard kind of moralistic or retrograde straight, or even mainstream gay, morality. I don't know that I've answered that question, as much as I want to pose the question.

Interviewer

I'm reminded again of the reading, when somebody asked a question to the effect of 'what do you think about drugs?' And basically what you said at the time is that you felt there was a period when drugs genuinely saved your life, in the sense that they were a thing that allowed you to escape something, at a time when if you hadn't been able to escape in that way, it would have killed you. But over time, that way to escape trauma in turn can become something that compounds the trauma itself, which seems to be a lot of what *Sketchtasy* is about.

Sycamore

The characters in *Sketchtasy*, they're doing drugs to escape the world. They want to be floating on the ceiling at all times, and yes, like you said, that enables them to create their own world, but it also compounds the trauma. And in my own life—I do think as a teenager drugs saved my life. Looking back, I can think of other things that I did not have access to that might have helped me… but I didn't have access to them, I had access to drugs. And there is that transition between saving my life, and becoming my life. For me, when I could see that they were becoming my life, I was like, 'I need to stop, I need to get out of this,' but not everyone has those self preservation skills in the same way.

I think in *Sketchtasy*, there's an open question. Drugs might still be the best choice for many of the characters in this book, regardless of the toll, because what are the other options?

Interviewer

To me, there's a way this ties back to that kind of affect we discussed, the false progressivism, or maybe in a broader way, to the assimilationist impulse you described earlier. This impulse can be a way to survive, and even appear to thrive, but in the end becomes traumatic, both to your own sense of self and to those around you.

Sycamore

Well, you asked earlier about *The Freezer Door*, and Seattle—Seattle is a perfect example of a city that believes in itself to the cost of actually creating a self that matters. There's so much of this sense of, 'we're on the cutting edge, we really are a truly equitable culture,' something like that. [Laughing] I can't even repeat the rhetoric, it's so depressing! Until like four years ago, people couldn't even say gentrification, and now, it's all about 'density.' The rhetoric of the gentrifiers has infiltrated the people who are allegedly against gentrification. That is the ultimate nightmare of neoliberalism.

When I say the white picket fence of the eyes, I mean walking around Seattle, that is how people look at you. It's the suburban imagination that's colonized the urban environment. Where people can live in these buildings, like upscale mid-rise apartment buildings where you drive in and never see anyone else and you live in a somewhat luxurious place with a nice view and great facilities to have parties on the roof and you think that's an urban life. An urban life is about what changes you in the world, it's about existing in public space, it's about the dynamic possibility and impossibility of connecting with people that you never imagined you would engage with. But that is not the city that we have now.

In one review of *Sketchtasy*, by Paul Constant in the *Seattle Review of Books*, he said that I'm a "chronicler of the life and death of American cities." And I love it when someone gives you insight into your own process in a review, because I think that is true. When I moved to Seattle, people kept asking me, 'are you going to write *The End of Seattle*,' and we are seeing changes in Seattle that in some ways are similar to the changes in San Francisco. But what is different is that Seattle was already a way more homogenized city—way more. Pre-gentrification Seattle was already more homogenous than gentrified San Francisco. So the changes we have here aren't *making* a homogenized city. They're taking away the little cracks in the armor of the gentrified city. They're smoothing them over and soon there'll be nothing.

I will say that one thing that happened on tour—and this is the first time this has ever happened—when I was in San Francisco, I was walking around in the street, and I could not feel it. Everything was quieter, there was no street culture, there was no graffiti, there was no interaction. I found myself one night walking to the neighborhood that had once formed me, the Mission. I had already avoided that neighborhood for, like, the last 10 years I was living in San Francisco, but it was the most formative neighborhood for me as a queer person, as a radical, as someone trying to create my own world in the ruins of everyday violence. And I found myself just walking there automatically, and I was really just looking for... not literal people that I knew, but people that I could feel like I might have something in common with. San Francisco has sheltered outsider cultures that are unimaginable in most US cities, and I could not feel it, I could not find those people, and it took me days to even feel like I was there. And I also felt the way people interacted with me in the street, which is that white picket fence in the eyes, and it felt like it was the same. It really was intense.

Boston, to me... when I'm writing about Boston in '95 in *Sketchtasy*, I'm writing about the worst version of a city. Smug and self satisfied. Boston sees itself as the cradle of liberalism. But in reality it's a city that is viciously afraid of difference. But, I feel like everywhere has become Boston. And in the same way, when I'm talking about Seattle now as a super homogeneous, smug and self-satisfied city that simultaneously is brutally pushing away anyone on the margins—that's everywhere too. And you have some exceptions, but everywhere these are the successful cities. And what do they do with that success? I think Seattle is a perfect example. To give a tiny little thing that I'm obsessed with, Seattle had this Ride Free area for the buses, starting in like 1980, where within a certain part of downtown, bus service was completely free. And in 2012, one of the most prosperous times in the history of Seattle, what does the city do? They end it!

That's what money gets you, it gets you an end of social services. It's so frightening. This is a city that finally is talking about a crisis in displacement and a crisis in homelessness and a lack of affordable housing, but how is the city trying to deal with it? With this rhetoric around 'density.' They say, 'oh, if we just increase the density, if we just upzone neighborhoods, then magically, affordable housing will appear!' But what actually happens is it's just giving more space to developers to build a bunch of overpriced garbage. The best example of that is Yesler Terrace, which was one of the largest housing projects in Seattle. It had large apartments, with entire families who had been living there for decades. People had vegetable gardens, mostly Asian and black families, many of them multigenerational, hundreds of people were living there. And they upzoned that area to tear down the projects, so Vulcan Construction (what a great name!) could build luxury high rises.

This is what frightens me so much in Seattle. People still believe this rhetoric! 'Oh, we just need more density.' Why don't you look at actual examples of what has happened in neighborhoods that have been upzoned? Does it actually create more affordable housing? No! So we need a new model. One great model would be to use this huge ditch across from city hall, which is owned by the city and is already in a neighborhood zoned for high rises... the tallest buildings in Seattle are all right there. Let's just say, conservatively, that they built a 50 story building with 50 units on each floor—that would be 2500 units, with an average of 1-2 people that they would immediately house, in low-income permanent housing—that would house about 4000 people. All you would need are two of those buildings and everyone who was homeless in Seattle would actually have a permanent home. Instead, what does the city do? They sold it, to a for-profit developer at below market rate. It just depresses me when people are obsessed with the wrong solution.

But also, when I came back here, after being in San Francisco, I was like, 'oh wait, there's more graffiti on the streets here!' Which just shocked me, because once there was no graffiti in Seattle, and I love graffiti. To me, graffiti is about connecting with the urban environment, looking for the messages. Especially these new stickers. The sticker graffiti in Seattle, suddenly it's political. In the past, it was mostly just people making a cute sticker, which I'm all for, but now there's all this different 'anti-bro' graffiti in the sticker tagging. There's 'Citizens for a Bro-Free Capitol Hill,' there's 'Trust No Bro," there's one with a yuck face and it says, 'yuck, bros!' There's one that just says 'fuck you techie!' [Laughing] These are good! And there's a whole series saying to reject something—reject transphobia, reject the gender binary, reject racism, reject borders.

So it's interesting, coming back here... you asked earlier, what does that feel like, and one thing that I do feel a sort of hopefulness is in the graffiti. Every dumpster is completely covered, like, *covered*, you know. I don't know why the dumpsters are so popular here. The dumpsters in San Francisco have no graffiti on them at this point. San Francisco has a really aggressive campaign against graffiti... friends of mine were telling me you could stencil something on the street and within hours it's gone, because they have a sandblaster out there.

Whenever people imagine a golden age, sometime in the past, it didn't exist. And if we're living in this country, the dominant colonial power in the world... any time that we're living in is a terrible time, right? And we have to create something else anyway. No matter when we're living or where we're living, I think that we have to create something else. The question has come up at some of the readings, 'so where should people be moving?' And I don't have the answer to that question. The actual answer is, we need to create that here-and-now, wherever we are.

Interviewer

In Seattle, at least, what would you like to see more of? What can we do interpersonally or politically right now to help steer things in the best possible direction?

Sycamore

The first thing is for people actually to interact with one another in the streets. The Seattle Freeze, you know, people act as if that is some sort of byproduct of Nordic heritage—but the number of Nordic people in Seattle is like under 10%. And I lived here in '96, '97, and that term did not exist. People were very friendly! It was actually one of the friendliest places I'd ever lived, at that point. That is a gentrification term, but people act as if it's something else. It's also related to the fact that we're living in darkness for 8 months of the year, so of course people become a little shut down, but let's push against that, you know. That's the first thing—people actually interacting with one another, across the lines of identity, in everyday experience. For me, that's why I live in a city. So much of my life takes place just walking around and looking at things, and wouldn't it be so much better if I could actually look at things with other people? Instead of gazing at stickers for a ray of hope.

And I think that sort of smug, self-righteous, 'we have arrived' mentality, which is so popular in Seattle, is gross. People have to let it go and see the city for what it is, you know—it's a dystopian tech company town. That doesn't mean that there aren't other possibilities, but until we actually see that reality… We also need to reject the rhetoric of the people who are destroying it. By that I mean Amazon, or Vulcan Construction—I just love saying that over and over again, 'Vulcan' Construction—I love the fact that Amazon and Vulcan Construction are two companies that are destroying our town. And people say, 'you know, but you can't be angry at them, they don't mean it…' well actually, they do mean it, that's why they're here. We need to reach beyond that.

I live on Capitol Hill, and most people know of the gentrification of Capitol Hill, in some sense at least—the tech boys, frat boys. But I think people don't consider it on a deeper level. This should be obvious, but the people who made Capitol Hill into what it is now were actually insiders, not outsiders. The mini-moguls, the restaurateurs, the people who started the Capitol Hill Block Party, the people who created this subculture as a commodity—those are the people to blame for what Seattle is now, and you can go to any neighborhood in Seattle and see there's a little group of people who are the ones who have benefitted, and at the same time they act like they don't like what's happened.

We need to look deeper. We need to get out of this rhetoric of like, garbage. The suffocating, silencing, slogan-obsessed, rhetoric around density—as soon as you say, 'Oh, I like density,' they've won. They've won, you know. The way that debate is framed is that there are people who are in favor of density, and then there are these rich people who just want to keep their homes. And those people certainly exist, but those are not the two sides! Those people are on the same side!

It's like, what density are we talking about? I think if we're gonna talk about density, we need to be talking about a density of lived experience, a density of meaningful interactions, a density of actually caring about one another, a density of prioritizing the people who are marginalized before the people who actually are privileged. There are some great things that have happened in Seattle, like the $15 minimum wage. That's something that's actually helped everyone. But what else can we do that actually would help everyone instead of just criminalizing, marginalizing, and brutalizing the people who are most vulnerable, while holding up everyone else?

There's this nonprofit here called Love City Love, and they basically turn vacant buildings into temporary dance space, more or less, dance or party or art spaces. I remember thinking, 'Well, that's kind of interesting,' and then I read this interview with the person who started it, and he said his motto is 'collaboration with gentrification.' This is not a joke, he literally said that.

Interviewer

Wow.

Sycamore

He's like, 'People in tech, they need art too! So in my dream world, we could have a Love City Love in the lobby of every one of these buildings.' But as soon as you're talking about collaboration with gentrification, you're just talking about putting a pretty face on homogenization. What we actually need to be talking about is destroying that mentality. This is such a rich city, there's so much money, and we know the billionaires are never going to actually... I mean, there's fucking Jeff Bezos, who could just take out his pocket change and say, 'I want everyone in Seattle to have free public transportation.' It would cost him, nothing, like *nothing*, and then everyone would love him! This is how demented these people are. 'I have so much money, the only thing I can think to do is like, send it to space'—that's literally his quote!

Interviewer

To tie it back to something you touched on very early—it's about accountability, right? All that anybody's really asking—well, I'd ask a lot more, but the most basic thing that people are asking—is that companies be at least vaguely accountable for the changes they're creating. If you're an entity that is changing everything around you—strip mining the culture of the city and using it to boost your business—you should have to contribute something back. And it seems that one thing people in Seattle really need, to return another of your earlier thoughts, is more honesty—about people's position in life, their position relative to others, what the structure of their lives is doing to the lives of the people around them.

Sycamore

One: obviously these people need to be forced to actually fork over their pocket change if we're going to have meaningful structural change. But, two: we shouldn't be swallowing their rhetoric and then turning it around and acting as if it was our own idea. People just vomit out the language of the oppressor, then they swallow it as progress. I mean, that might save you money, because if you eat your own vomit, you don't have to spend much on groceries, but in the end [laughing], you're gonna die of malnutrition!

—<o>—

The Garden

Kamari Bright

And in that moment

when he saw her

partake of the angel that

WAS the "forbidden fruit"

of the tree of God,

Adam realized he

was inadequate.

Naked.

He saw what the woman

pulled from his body

knew long before, that

he was dim and

dirt-made. That the angel

was her own piece of

forever to consume, while

he was merely her

limitation in paradise.

And Adam felt the heave

of *less-than* like the first

heart that ever broke,

then told Eve to

put some fucking clothes on.

—<o>—

Three Bullets

J. C. Sibara

We met on a corner in downtown Portland, where the electric train used to end. I could have pretended not to hear the old man. I usually ignored men who talked to me on the street. But this one spoke with a Slavic accent that sounded like my grandfather's. Unlike it, too, though I couldn't quite place how.

"What is happening to the library?" He asked, pausing between words.

I had the same question. It was my first trip to the library since I had come home from the Bay Area to take care of my Deda two months earlier. Yellow construction tape blocked the entrance. The roof was torn away, the building's innards exposed to the sky. The stone carcass loomed, casting uneven shadows on the nearby shops and sidewalks. A sign announced a temporary library located on 4th and Columbia. The new and improved library would re-open in 1997, three years away. *Internet*, the poster promised. Outlets for laptop computers, central air conditioning, wall-to-wall carpeting, even an espresso bar. I didn't care about these innovations. Having just lost Deda, this felt like another death.

The library had been my second home in high school. I passed my afternoons in the high-ceilinged reading room flipping through old newspapers on microfiche, listening to scratchy recordings of Billie Holiday and Ella Fitzgerald, or hiding out in the fluorescent-lit stacks with my girlfriend. The only place we felt safe to touch each other was inside that maze of disintegrated scaffolding and bowing bookshelves, despite the heavy marble floors that threatened collapse. It seemed just the right place, now that Deda was gone and I needed to figure out what to do next with my life. That morning my roommate in Berkeley had called about the lease. Would I be returning for another year?

Or would I stay, and continue seeing Milena? Her family, like mine, lived in the Serbian community our grandparents formed in Southeast Portland after World War II. Milena had trailed three years behind me in school so I didn't pay her much attention while we were growing up. As adults, the gap closed. One evening shortly after my arrival in Portland, our families gathered for a meal, and during our post-dinner hour in the kitchen, she grabbed my wrist as I reached past her for the Brillo. We soon slipped into a togetherness without naming it. But ever since Deda's funeral, I'd been avoiding her, unsure what to say about our future.

"The library has moved," I said to the man. "That way. A mile or so." I pointed toward the river.

The man stared at the sign, his shoulders slumped. He wore several layers of brown and grey wool and his forehead only reached my chin.

"I do not understand the directions," he said.

"Where are you from?" I stopped myself from asking. It would have sounded so American.

What are you? People used to ask my grandfather, and he would say, *A dragon.*

"Will you call the library for me?" the man asked. He nodded toward the phone booth across the street. "I have a question and maybe it is too far to walk."

I thought of Deda then, having to ask over and over in his precise but accented English, *Can you please repeat that?* or *More slowly, please.*

"Of course," I said to the man. "What do you need to ask?"

"The address of the Pope," he said. "I need to send him a message."

I crossed my arms. He must be a Croat, I thought.

He wasn't the first I'd met, but the others were younger, and generations removed—like the girl at my high school, a Croatian's great-great granddaughter who cheerfully announced to me her heritage when she found out, during first-year orientation, that my family was also from Yugoslavia. We might have been enemies if we had grown up in the Balkans. But I couldn't blame her. I knew little more than she did. Deda kept the details of the genocide just behind his teeth, only letting slip, under his breath, an occasional curse against the "Ustaše." When I was twelve I asked my father who the Ooh-stah-shay were, and he said they were like the Nazis, only Croatian, and then made an excuse to leave the room. As soon as I learned how to use a card catalog, I began to teach myself the answers instead of pestering my family with questions.

"You could just write 'Vatican City'?" I said to the man, who seemed old enough to have been one of Hitler's cronies.

"I do not want the letter to get lost," he said. "I will find a quarter." He reached into a tattered Nordstrom shopping bag. When he let go of one of the handles, I thought his entire life's possessions might spill out. But there was no Ustaša coat of arms, no Swastika, only an English-language Bible and a few other worn books and papers. He drew a quarter from the jumble, held it out to me, and nodded toward the phone booth again.

I stared at the quarter, wondering if there was some way I could get out of this. Perhaps I could just tell him I was Serbian. But since the wars had broken out in '92, and each day brought new stories of atrocities by those who might be third or fourth cousins ("Propaganda," Deda insisted), it had become a habit not to mention my origins. Besides, hadn't I given him my word? I plucked the coin from his fingers and strode across the street, the man following a few steps behind.

I did not expect him to join me in the glass booth, but holding the door open wide with his elbow, he entered, turning to press against my side. Blood burned in my ears. I could smell pipe tobacco on his breath, mothballs on his coat. Deda sometimes stood closer to people in public than they did to one another, but this man's hovering felt extreme. I reassured myself that I'd had Self Defense in college. Figured I could break his birdlike nose if I had to. But as his fingers fluttered against my back, a memory came to me, of how, when I was a girl, my grandfather would sit with me by the fire and shake my waist-long black hair dry with his hands.

During this ritual Deda would keep me still with stories, like the one about the ferocious she-dragon disguised as a damsel. She looked into a mirror, and thinking the reflection someone else, fell in love with her own image. While the damsel was distracted, a poor man stole the single red strand from her headful of raven hair. He sold it to the emperor for a thousand gold sequins. The emperor split the hair open and discovered written upon it the most remarkable stories from olden times.

I felt my companion reach into his bag. He handed me a pen and paper napkin. It seemed an invitation to write down one of Deda's stories, but I looked up the number for the main library and dialed, my call forwarded automatically to the temporary branch. I asked for a reference librarian.

"How can I help you?"

"Oh, um, do you know—my friend would like the Pope's address. Can you look that up... for him?"

"It's right here in the World Almanac," the librarian responded brightly, as if she heard this question every day. I felt my ears heat up again, this time in shame rather than fear, as I transcribed "His Holiness" and "Apostolic Palace" onto the napkin.

Done, I thought, returning the receiver to its cradle. I turned halfway toward the man and shoved the pen and napkin toward him. The napkin fluttered to the floor before he could catch it. We both stared down. He had to back out of the phone booth so I could lean over to pick up the napkin. He accepted it with both hands, which were white from the cold, his fingers long and thin, his nails smooth and yellow. Our hands touched, and in that moment I felt myself commit to him for as long as he needed my help. I held out the pen, too, but he put up his hand. "You keep it."

"No, I couldn't possibly," I said. It was a fountain pen of the expensive mail-order variety.

"I insist," he said, and then: "Come with me to the copy shop. I need to make a copy for the Pope. It is only a few blocks." I slid the pen into my pocket.

As we walked along the abandoned train tracks, he told me he had recently come from Bosnia. I gulped a fast, full breath, grateful that I hadn't given myself away. He was probably a refugee. Many were applying for asylum—the immigration officers played darts on the map and this was where he landed. But I knew from the relief group my parents helped organize that most of the refugees were going to St. Louis or Chicago, Toronto or Montreal. I asked how he got to Oregon. He said his daughter immigrated in the 1980s. When the war broke out, she pleaded with him to come over. But she worked long hours at a hospital, he explained, so he spent a lot of time exploring the city on his own.

"I like Portland very much," he said.

"You don't mind the rain?"

I was thinking of the black-and-white photograph on my grand-father's bedside table. My grandmother, in a modest bathing suit, splashed in the Adriatic, miles of white pebbles glistening in the background. Deda took the photo a few years before she was killed and he and my father escaped to America.

Deda looked at that photo often in his final days, while my parents and I took turns sitting with him, adjusting his pillows and blankets—ostensibly to make sure he was comfortable, but really to distract ourselves from his swift-approaching end. A week before he died, as I sat at his bedside, Deda told me how he lost her.

At first he seemed in a reverie, gazing at the photo, until his eyes snapped toward mine, alert. From the binding of his Bible he drew a small golden key emblazoned with Cyrillic script, and handed it to me.

He pointed to the top drawer of his desk. "Open it," he said. Inside lay a small pistol with a dark wood paneled handle, an antique. The weapon's presence shocked me. My parents were avowed pacifists. But Deda said, "This will be yours. It is time you learned how to care for it." He told me where to find the solvent and lubricant, brushes and cloths, stored in a deeper drawer. I laid them out on the desk, along with a velvet drawstring bag whose contents clinked when I set it down.

Deda pulled his blankets back. He drew his legs to the side of the bed and pushed himself up. He adjusted his pajamas, his breaths shallow and rasping. Setting his feet on the floor, he leaned from the bed and reached into the top drawer to retrieve the pistol. I noticed he was careful not to point the muzzle toward me or touch the trigger.

"Always check first," he said, and showed me how to remove the magazine. "My cousin gave me this gun. He told me we needed protection. He lived much closer to town, so he knew before I did that danger was on its way."

I watched as Deda disassembled the rest of the pistol.

"The day I heard trucks roll into the village, I knew it was them. The Ustaše."

He and my father, then just a small boy, were inside the house, Deda said, but my grandmother was out in the garden. Deda caught her eye through the window and nodded toward the back of the house, signaling her to join them under the rear porch, behind the false wall in the cellar.

Now Deda was soaking a cloth with solvent. "Open the window," he told me. "The fumes." There came a sharp, sweet odor of alcohol tinged with bananas.

"She saw me," Deda said, as he began wiping down each of the pistol's parts. "She nodded." So he'd turned away from the window, picked up my father, and taken him to the hideout.

"But she didn't come," he said. Over another cloth he drizzled linseed oil.

"I heard boots," he said. He was rubbing the oiled cloth over each of the gun's pieces now. The footfalls, he told me, were like thunder entering the house, my grandmother's steps like rain behind them. Two men's voices asked where her husband was. "Out," she answered, "foraging for mushrooms."

"The boy, too?" they said.

"Yes," said my grandmother. "They'll be gone for hours."

Deda paused then. Because I am a woman, I understood what happened next. He didn't have to say it.

I watched him reassemble the pistol. He placed it in my hand, held his own over mine as he showed me how, if it was loaded, I would cock and fire it.

"Show me you can do all this on your own," he said.

I repeated each step of the gun's use and care, guided by his steady words. The first time I tried to draw the hammer back, it did not engage, and slid forward again, the shlock of it resounding in the room.

"After that," he said, resuming his story, "I heard a single shot. And felt it here." He drew his finger to his chest.

We both looked at the photograph of my grandmother, who likely understood she was giving her body and her life for the possibility of mine.

"Again," he commanded after a moment's pause, and I went through the cycle of care once more. When I finished, I handed the pistol back to him, my hands steadier after the second try.

"This is good," Deda said, checking my work. He set the gun down next to the picture frame. He pulled his legs back into the bed and drew the blankets up. He reached for the velvet bag.

"Hold these," he said, pulling the string loose and shaking three rounds into my palm. The metal casings were cool to the touch. He drew each one from my hand and loaded it into the magazine as he told me his regrets: He hadn't gotten his family out of Croatia sooner. He hadn't shot those Ustaše men before they got to my grandmother. He hadn't avenged her death before fleeing through groves and mountains to Partisan territory and then to America with his son.

"Your father was too young to remember," Deda said. "I've never told him, and he's never asked. But I'm telling you, because you need to know." He handed me the loaded pistol and motioned for me to lock it in the drawer.

Paused at a stoplight with my Croatian companion, I closed my fingers around the fountain pen. I imagined Deda under the porch, one hand over my young father's mouth, the other clutching that pistol. What if he had leapt out to save her?

"Why talk about rain on a day such as this?" The old man waved his arm at the cloudless sky.

At the copy shop, he asked me to duplicate Deuteronomy VI for him. He handed me his Bible but I handed it right back.

"You turn the pages," I said. Just the day before I had taken Communion at a backyard service of the new Serbian Orthodox church my grandfather helped to found. It didn't feel right to touch a Croatian's Bible.

The man opened the book and flipped through it. Several one and five dollar bills appeared, sandwiched like bookmarks between the pages.

"How many copies?" I asked, once he settled on a passage.

"Mmm, a lot," he said. "Twenty-four."

I showed him how to line the book up with the ruler on the glass. He covered one side with a loose piece of paper left behind by another customer, blank except for a handwritten sum: $14.00. This appeared on all our copies, next to verse 5: "And thou shalt love the Lord thy God, with all thine heart, and with all thy soul, and with all thy might." I recognized this verse from a Jewish theology course I'd taken in college.

"I wish to remind the Pope of a special message," he said. He pulled out one of his smooth five dollar bills and headed to the cashier.

I walked with him along the tracks to the post office. Leaning against the counter, he folded a few of the photocopied pages and tucked them into an envelope.

"Don't you want to write a note?" I asked, picturing an attendant in Vatican City opening the envelope and leafing through the duplicate copies, looking for an appeal.

"He will understand." He handed me one of the copied pages. "For you," he said. While we stood in line to buy a stamp, I read some of the other verses on the page, in which Moses instructs the Israelites to tell their sons why they should honor the laws and decrees of God. He liberated their people from slavery in Egypt so that He could give them the land He had sworn to their fathers. Which land did my companion imagine God had sworn to his people, I wondered, and what would Deda have thought about that?

Letter on its way, we walked out into the chill air. I glanced down the street for an East Side bus. He put on a pair of sunglasses that swallowed his face and made him look like a fly.

"You are very beautiful," he said. He began pulling my fingers. Ungloved, they were cold. "Please will you have a cup of coffee with me?" He said his favorite cafe was Nordstrom's. "The coffee is cheap and the waitresses will let us sit as long as we like."

I looked at my watch. A headache was spreading across my forehead from the sun's glare.

"I have to go," I said. "Thanks, anyway." I smiled and began to turn away, but he took my hand and pressed it against his dry lips.

"Bless you, bless you," he said.

His breath was hot on my skin. Something fierce leapt from my stomach to my hand and I slid my fingers around his wrist and dug them into the wool. He gasped. His frame was so light I could have lifted him. I imagined crushing him, stabbing him with the pen, his pen. Instead, I leaned over and, aiming for his right cheekbone, grazed the corner of his sunglasses, leaving a blurry lipstick smudge.

"*Prijatelj*," I said, and kissed his left cheek.

I knew he would recognize the word—it meant the same thing in Croatian, too. But in case he didn't hear my grandfather's Serbian song in how I spoke the word, I gave him one final kiss on the right cheek and then released his arm. We stared at each other, his eyes gaping with fear and amazement. He must have recognized me in that instant as both a new friend and an old enemy.

That evening, my parents out at church, I invited Milena over. I opened one of Deda's vintage wines and poured her a glass. I told her how I missed my grandfather singing when he worked in the garden, his stories.

"Do you remember the one about the dragon—"

Milena laughed and finished my sentence: "Who devoured a prince?"

I drew her close, pressed my lips to her ear and wondered if, in time, I could love her as my grandfather had loved my grandmother. Maybe I would love her more.

Later that evening, as she fastened the buttons of her blouse in the dim glow of my bedroom reading light, Milena confessed, "I was kind of relieved when my grandparents died. They were fanatical. The past is the past. I'm an American."

"You knew them both," I replied, my throat tight.

In a gentler tone, she asked, "What do you know about her?"

I led Milena into Deda's room and showed her the photo of my grandmother. Milena studied it for a long moment, then looked at my face, traced my cheekbones and chin with the edge of her thumb. I pulled the key from Deda's Bible and unlocked his top desk drawer. Earlier in the evening, before Milena arrived, I had opened the drawer and removed the pistol's rounds, tucked them back into the velvet bag. No one needed a gun loaded against regrets in the house. I handed her the pistol now and watched as she ran her fingers over it. Her red nails and the barrel flashed in the light from Deda's lamp as she turned it over to examine the other side.

"Do you think he ever used it?" she asked, handing the pistol back to me.

"I don't know," I said.

—<o>—

Quantifiable

Dawn Pichón Barron

I.

Did you know there are 27 bones in one human hand?
If those 27 comprise a quarter of all the bones in one human,
And supposing a human has two hands, thus half the bones of
Our human are located in the hands—hands that love or
Kill with half the bones of the body—like if we had our Indian
Bones or Irish bones in just our hands, were measured by
Our capable hands

II.

If the average human heart thumps around 100,000 beats a day
Pumping 2000 gallons of blood through its preciousness,
Does the heart know when the blood is our colonizer blood
Or other? Can the heart feel the forces of oppressed and oppressor;
The story of bloods mixing? But more importantly, does the pure-blood
Feel different as it cruises up and into the heart, leaving just the same
Our broken hearts

III.

Do the experts truly know the brain holds as much data as a 64-gigabyte
iPhone?

Information from past, present, and possibly the future—if one believes
Outside the scope of tangible—If the data were translated to sound, and
Echolocation practiced, could we find ourselves in reflected sound waves?
Can we program what data we keep, and what we destroy, or replace with
Stories from ancestors, awakened by our calling
Our muscle-memory

IV.
No other in the mammalian world has the uvula dangling in the back of the
Mouth with its precious cargo, packed cavity of nerves and muscle and bone
The uvula would be proof enough, yes, that all humans are the same
Placing to bed, under a spell to never wake, atrocities of other
Heart swells with blood and belonging, bones of hands unmarked,
Brains powered by such knowledge, the past
Our forced swallow

V.
On average, a human takes around 20,000 breaths a day
Breathing in the air-memory of the land and history, breath held inside until
Released, and what if each breath carried a piece of self
Entered another and another, for no single breath can find a home
No ownership or allotment, no safe passage as breath would tell the story
Our legacy

—<o>—

Lucy's Midnight Story

Ian Denning

At midnight, Lucy rolls over and asks "Did you hear about Sadie?"

My wife likes to tell me stories about made-up people. We are staying with her parents in New York, fighting again about where we ought to live: New York or Seattle, near her family or mine. The argument is as old as our relationship, but in the stale, overwarm air of her parents' apartment, it feels much older. I'm grateful for the distraction.

"No, I haven't heard about Sadie," I say. This is part of the ritual. "Tell me about her."

"Well," Lucy says, "Sadie was a masseuse at the resort. Giving all those old guys massages—no happy endings. But one winter she slipped and fell in the parking lot and threw out her back."

"That's awful," I say.

"So she got addicted to prescription pain pills. She was spending a *lot* of time in her house, you know, not answering her friends calls, feeling really sorry for herself, doing a lot of drugs. Then, one day, she was high on pills and she went out to get her mail, and she slipped and fell again! Right on her ass! And as she sat there, writhing around on the ground, she saw the opening to a tunnel—right there in the snowbank next to her mailbox."

"That's weird, right? There's not normally a tunnel there?"

"No, it was a new tunnel," Lucy says. "And Sadie was very attracted to it. 'Where does this tunnel next to my mailbox lead?' she wondered. So she crawled inside. The walls were made out of ice, like all blue and sparkly. She had to go on hands and knees at first, and as she crawled, she started to hear techno music. *Dum dum dum dum dum.* And the walls started opening up and the tunnel got wider, until she could stand up and walk. *Dum dum dum dum dum.* And then it opened up into a room.

"She was standing on a ledge, and the room was full of the night sky. There were stars. Sadie stood at the edge of the tunnel and she moved her hand through the sky, swirling the stars around. They flowed up into her arms and she felt very warm. She was glowing from the inside. Then, she leaned too far over and fell in. She fell and fell and fell and fell."

Lucy goes quiet for a moment. In the other room, her parents are watching an old Peter Lorre movie. They eat at midnight, stay up and wake late, take their walk through Riverside Park. Regular days extending in front of them *ad infinitum*, a marriage caught between two mirrors.

"And at first it was scary, feeling all those stars rush past," Lucy says, "but then she relaxed, and she started to enjoy the falling."

I ask her what happened next, but she has already fallen asleep.

—◇—

When Will We Ache Less

Michelle Peñaloza

from a desert in Nevada   a man launches flowers
into space

just now I thought: why   when you are closer
am I more lonely?

     (the you
         could be anyone)

maybe distance is what I equate   with love

you are away and I am   alone with the bullfrogs
and crickets and raccoons
     that pull up the new sod like carpet
their child fingers searching for
                  grubs in moonlight

elsewhere white men chant
    you will not replace us

why is being born white
    in America not enough?

above me the geese form haphazard
     V   V
             V   floating over the house
loose victories each twilight
         paraded from one sewage pond
to the other across town
         they don't leave the valley for winter

     ~

this world and what comes from   our garden is too much

abundance is a burden of responsibility
this rash of tomatoes appears and reappears
with so little effort   with so little to do with me

what is it like to be everywhere
        to be seen and heard and known and believed
with so little effort   with so little to do with you

     ~

I collect facts

        facts are marbles in my mouth
how to hold each one   how to keep
how to speak how to scream with so much to contain

my mouth grows bigger and bigger

butcher birds hold their prey
to dismember   they cacti their knife and larder

26 young Nigerian women
were fished from the Mediterranean and dried as headlines
and disappeared again

bullets shot from an AR-15   move through bodies
like boats   exits wounds the size of oranges

hyenas eat ghosts   that wander the streets
they eat the bones the butchers' sons and sons and sons
feed them from their hands

someone found a grasshopper   stuck
among van Gogh's olive trees   trapped 128 years

        ~

dragonflies hover over the kiddie pool we soak in   to beat the heat
thrips burnish a thousand holes into a row of bright green leaves
the scuttle of skinks along the fence line   sings feline   a rolodex of r's

        a raccoon just made
carcass   splayed across the road
        the cattle wires come alive   with feathered gargoyles
spread wings follow each speeding car
                every hour more wings   sky-full
                                        coast on warm carrion-wind
I could measure the days this way

name after name after name
the raccoon   a meat balloon fur crumple
                                disappearing

                disappearing

A Conversation with Quenton Baker

Interviewed by Dujie Tahat, Fall 2018 · Seattle, WA

Quenton Baker is a poet, educator, and Cave Canem fellow. His work has appeared in *Jubilat*, *Vinyl*, *Apogee*, *Poetry Northwest*, *Pinwheel*, and *Cura,* as well as in the anthologies *Measure for Measure: An Anthology of Poetic Meters* and *It Was Written: Poetry Inspired by Hip-Hop*. A 2017 Jack Straw Fellow and a former Made at Hugo House fellow, as well as the recipient of the 2016 James W. Ray Venture Project Award and the 2018 Arts Innovator Award from Artist Trust, Baker is the author of *This Glittering Republic* (Willow Books, 2016). He has an MFA in Poetry from the University of Southern Maine.

Interviewer

Let's start from the beginning—did you grow up in the Northwest?

Baker

I did. I'm from Seattle, born and raised on Beacon Hill.

Interviewer

How has growing up in the Northwest has influenced your writing?

That's an interesting question. I was at Cave Canem recently and I was talking with a friend there about the places I'd lived—Seattle. Portland, Maine. Portland, Oregon. These somewhat secluded places, not like New York or Chicago, the places where poets usually congregate. My friend was like 'It makes sense you were in those places because you have larger sensibilities; it makes sense that you would go to those places where you could be secluded and write.' I was like, "thank you." [laughs] I don't write about Seattle as a place, or I rarely do—I have a couple poems. But in terms of what I've learned here, and how my experience has structured my thinking—in that way, it shows up in my work.

Interviewer

It's interesting you started with Cave Canem—a lot of your work is engaged with blackness and anti-blackness and you come from the Northwest, a region that's very white. There are very few black people here, relative to everywhere else. Are those things related?

Baker

Historically, if you wanted to find Black people in Seattle you could go to the few neighborhoods where Black people could live. If we wanted to find each other, it was easier to do that. That's the reality of being inside a pocket around which a larger reality is built. That level of anti-blackness, and the level of whiteness that constitutes daily life in Seattle, it's impossible to escape. Maybe you can find a pocket dimension, but you can't escape that universe.

Interviewer

Your work is very much about the external—not autobiographical work, but writing contextually. So then that dynamic of being a small pocket in this bigger thing—in some way, is that autobiographical? Is that the link between the two for you?

Baker

Autobiography in poems is complicated. I've only lived my life; my experiences inform the themes I'm interested in. In terms of a specific experience of the American context, my poems are absolutely autobiographical. It's an autobiography because of the nature of anti blackness it's diffused in a certain way and spread out.

Interviewer

Who are your poems for?

Baker

Toni Morrison said 'Write the Books you want to read.' That's always stuck with me. I primarily write for myself, and for myself abstracted. My work is for anyone who has an understanding of, and genuine stake in, black interiority outside of the white imagination. Blackness as disconnected from the semiotics and the kind of meaning making and myth-meaning that has over-determined it from the outside. To paraphrase Fanon; outside of the violence, outside of the trauma, and outside of the pain, outside of the death inherent in Black life, there's also the lived reality of living inside that kind of breach. When I think about who I'm writing for, it's for the people living that, for the people who can value black life outside of the white imagination.

My process has changed a lot. When I was working on my first book, I really hadn't been writing poems very long. I came from the Rap world. I really wasn't doing poems before I went to grad schools. I don't know how I got into grad school... People are stupid? Or generous? They were like "this fool needs help!" [laughs]

Really, I didn't start writing poems seriously until I was working on a thesis. I was moving in all of these different directions. For *This Glittering Republic*, there were these themes burning inside me. I was reading wildly to try to find things to anchor them to. I was trying put that into a cohesive, coherent poetics. As I moved away from that project, it's been like, "how do I focus this? How do I really narrow in on something?"

Interviewer

Have you come to an answer?

Baker

I started writing long poems. The project I'm working on is a long, dedicated specific project. Whereas my book wasn't conceived of as a collection, or with a shape of everything in mind. But now that's the mode I'm working in.

Interviewer

Given the heaviness of what you write about, I imagine it's emotionally exhausting. How do you take care of yourself?

Baker

I get that question a lot, and every time it surprises me. I forget about that part. The way I see it, my job is to write. I was lucky enough once to meet Fred Moten, whom I greatly admire. After a reading, we were going out for drinks and I made a joke about self-care. He was like "I should go to sleep," and I said, "Oh yeah, Self Care is important." He looked at me and laughed like the concept of self-care was the most ridiculous thing in the world. It's real, but nah… I don't do a very good job.

Interviewer

For me, in my personal experience, and in the immigrant narrative, this compounds the inability to ease. You can't let up. It's hard to shift your state of mind, to take care of yourself, to regenerate in order to do more and better stuff.

Baker

The thing I've started to learn about myself is that when I feel so run down and worn to the nub, I feel that my language isn't as sharp. When the work starts to suffer, I know I need to take care of myself. As I was told once, I am my own instrument. It's not taking care of myself, it's taking care of the work. That's probably not very healthy but it's where I'm at right now.

Interviewer

What do you when the language isn't sparkling for you, when it's not bewildering in the way you want it to be? How do you get back to that state?

Baker

I read. Sometimes I just don't do anything... Watch some shit on Netflix, turn my brain off, but mostly it's reading. Because I want to be in language all the time. Sometimes, though, I don't want that language to challenge me, so I'll read a novel for pleasure, or some comic books. If I can work but my language isn't working, I'll read something on the long list of texts I need to get through for research.

Interviewer

Speaking of reading, who are some of the poets in your literary family tree?

Baker

That's my favorite question. I think the most important thing a poet can do is locate yourself in a lineage. For me, that's Gwendolyn Brooks; NJ Loftis; Lorenzo Thomas; Lucille [Clifton], of course; Audre [Lorde], her essays and her poems—her poems slap, "Black Unicorn" is crazy; Fred Moten;

Dawn Lundy Martin; Harryette Mullen; Aimé Césaire—there's this long
tradition of black radical writers that I really appreciate—Ishmael Reed;
Frantz Fanon.

There are so many people who made my work possible. That's why it's so
important to find a lineage. If someone asks "Who's part of your lineage?
Who's your work in conversation with?" and you can't come back with a
list of, like, fifty names… that's a signal. I don't mean to be deterministic
or prescriptive for other people, but it's so important for me to locate
myself within that. That means everything. Like Jack Spicer says, "poems
echo and correspond." He was talking about his own work. But I think
that's true, generally speaking too. Whether I know or it or not, I'm in
conversation with all these other people who made me possible. I want to
be talking to them.

In the project I'm working on now, I borrow a lot of lines from people—
Nate Mackey and others—to highlight the specific ways my work was
made possible by theirs.

Interviewer

You've talked a lot about black literary tradition, carving out space, locating
yourself. Cave Canem is known for that. What did you get out of it?

Baker

It was phenomenal. We were talking earlier of being in a pocket.
Here, all of the sudden you're not in a pocket, but an entire universe.
And experiencing the complete absence of those semiotics that often
determine black life was so profound. Through society, you've experienced
racial trauma, gender-related trauma. Those contexts are always present,
encroaching in a violent way. You start to think that the ways in which
you defend yourself and survive are your personality. It's rare and often

impossible to be away from all that—for me it had never happened until I went to Cave Canem.

When you are away from those contexts, for me it was shocking to see what parts of myself are still intact, and what parts of myself still unreachable. What just can't exist in so many other contexts. It was profound. Wow, I can actually exist, in public in the world around people and not be in survival mode. That was crazy for me.

Interviewer

I think often of how form is really tied to non-dominant expression, to speaking into dominance. I'm fascinated with how you keep a relationship to language. How do you keep yourself alert? How does it continue to sparkle? There is a long tradition of how form is married to those words—to that radical expression. In a way, form and language are the same. There's no real distinction between the two, because of the way they are laid out on the page. Because of the word blue. B-L-U-E. Constructed the way it is on this page, in relation, in space, to all the other words… suddenly, I'm looking at this word that I've seen a million times before, in a different way.

Baker

You said it: language is form.

When you ask me about form… I have to turn it; I don't think of them as separate. That's absolutely right. I like your word "bewilderment." The word I use is "surprise." But I might steal your word— I like "bewilderment" better!

Interviewer

I'm sure I've stolen that from someone…

We all steal from each other; that's how it works. To me, "surprise" is what drives everything. It needs to be earned, but that's at the heart of a poem.

One of the forms you do play with in your book, *This Glittering Republic*, is the contrapuntal poem. I thought it was interesting: a couple of the columns were almost—not clichés—but simple statements, that you could hear in a pop form. I'm curious, what are you trying to do, with a contrapuntal? I'd love to get through your process of writing one.

I love contrapuntal poems. There's this Yusef Komunyakaa poem in *Warhorses*, 'The Towers'. I think that was the first contrapuntal poem that really—[makes pop sound]— that really blew my top off. Because it's really hard to make a 9/11 poem. It's rather radical to write a poem for anything that big. The way he used that space and that breach really interested me.

Since then I have tried to write them. What interested me is that you are writing across a breach. Before I knew what that was, it called to me on a primal level. That's how Black folks live in this world—across, and through, and interrupting a breach.

This project I'm working on, I called them "omni-directions." They're like contrapuntal poems on steroids. It became an obsession of mine to write across that breach. That's what interested me: "Can I put this cliché-ass language in here?" It became like an alchemical process. What is this breach doing to language?

Interviewer

I'm also fascinated by the way you play with space. The contrapuntal is reliant on that breach space. Given our discussion about form, the way things live in relation to space—what are you doing with space?

Baker

Yeah. I had to learn that the space is part of the poem, that the space is mine to use with intention in every poem. That poem where space is an example, or the Surrender poem serves as that breach; it became like a preposition, or a noun, or an adjective. It became part of the language I had to use, the language of absence, the language of a breach, of a negation, or a removal. All of those things that can be contained in language but may be better contained in space.

Interviewer

We talked about how, before your MFA, you were primarily into Rap. You were in that anthology, *Poetry Inspired by Hip-hop*. What is the relationship between the two for you?

Baker

There's a very close relationship. Hip-hop, rap verses are primarily accentual meter. You have four strong stresses to approximate the four-beat measure. For me, it inculcated a sense of rhythm and also the importance of rhythm in that language. When you're writing, you're writing to an instrument which is different than composing poems. There's an interior music to the actual syllables themselves which you have to be attuned to, and I carry that with me into poetry. There's just that play—the interior music of the syllable and the line and all of the different sound units, or sound and sense units.

When I'm writing a verse, typically I'm writing in four bar measures. At the end of the fourth bar, that's where the image or the punch line is. Working in those sound and sense units really honed how I wanted to approach poetry. That shit makes sense; that shit makes sense to me.

Interviewer

Even without knowing you have a hip-hop background, reading your poems—there's a real sonic force to them. Reading them out loud changes the game a bit. In crafting them, where does reading out loud fit in the process for you?

Baker

It ranks—there's like 1a and 1b. I always read my poems as I'm writing them. That's part of my process. It has to sound right, it has to look right, it has to read right, and it has sound right. All of that shit has to work together. That's another deviation from hip-hop; it doesn't matter how it looks on the page. Towards the end of my rap career, I started writing verses only in my head.

I don't always write in my head, but it always starts in the same way. The first composition is always in my head, and then goes to the page. That interplay is what I think helps the sound. The reason why I started writing rap verses in my head is because I found that when I was writing them on the page, it was too regular, the rhythm was too regular. I needed to agitate that.

People are always surprised when I have an Ann Carson epigraph in a poem about rap shit. You didn't expect range, motherfucker?

—<>—

Transient

Quenton Baker

Some [stars] are there but some burned out
ten thousand years ago… You see memories.
—Anne Carson

We built gods
real slick-smooth
big god-looks
on that stage
big god-breath
big god-sweat
the bass pumped
like priest-shrieks
like pure ghost
had climbed up
in church hat
in blue dress
the pews full
but none sat
in god's house

the fake dark
the track lights
the sound man
he's drunk but
we're gods
we built us
this big sound
this black shit
the trunk-thump
of raw truth
we built us
we bang drums
we sing loud
we're break beats
we're hands up!
the whole crowd
is white-faced
but who cares
you paid ten
but so what
your head nods
for my beats
your arms up
for my words
your drunk dap
for my fist
your drunk lips
for my lips
your scrunched fives
for my wax
your drunk love
in drunk eyes

for my swag
for my steez
that I know
is dead light.

Contributors.

Tara Atkinson *(Who Chooses)* is the author of two books—*Bedtime Stories* (alice blue books) and *Boyfriends* (Instant Future). Her work has appeared in *Hobart, City Arts Magazine, Fanzine, HTML Giant, The Iowa Review*, and elsewhere. She co-founded the independent literature festival, APRIL, and served as Managing Director from 2011 to 2016. She lives in Seattle with her husband, the painter Justin Duffus.

Anis Gisele *(First Lady)* is a recipient of fellowships and awards from VONA/Voices, Everyday Feminism, 4Culture, Artist Trust, King County, Hugo House, and Jack Straw Cultural Center, among other institutions. They come from Manila, Philippines, and currently live in Seattle.

Ruby Hansen Murray *(A Couple Walks Up the Logging Road)* is a writer and photographer living in the lower Columbia River estuary. Her work appears or is forthcoming in *As/Us, World Literature Today, Yellow Medicine Review, Apogee, The Rumpus*, and *American Ghost: Poets on Life after Industry*. She's the winner of 2017 Montana Prize in Creative Nonfiction, and has been awarded residencies at Hedgebrook, Ragdale, Playa, Vermont Studio Center, Virginia Center for the Creative Arts, and the Island Institute in Sitka. A fellow of the Jack Straw Writers Program, Fishtrap: Writing the West and VONA, Murray studied at Warren Wilson College and received an MFA from the Institute of American Indian Arts. She's a citizen of the Osage Nation with West Indian roots.

John Englehardt *(Be Okay, It Will Be Okay)* is a Seattle-based fiction writer whose work can be found in *The Stranger, Sycamore Review, The James Franco*

Review, and *Vol. 1 Brooklyn.* An instructor at Hugo House, his debut novel, *Bloomland,* is forthcoming from Dzanc Books in Fall 2019.

Kelli Russell Agodon *(On Learning the Galaxy Take Both Cash and Credit)* was a Finalist for the Washington State Book Awards and shortlisted for the Julie Suk Prize in Poetry for her most recent book, *Hourglass Museum* (White Pine Press, 2014). Her other books include *The Daily Poet: Day-By-Day Prompts For Your Writing Practice* and *Letters from the Emily Dickinson Room,* Winner of the Foreword Book of the Year Prize for poetry and also a Washington State Book Award Finalist. Agodon is the cofounder of Two Sylvias Press and the Co-Director of Poets on the Coast: A Weekend Writing Retreat for Women in Washington State.

Jessica Mooney *(Close Encounters)* has received grants from 4Culture and the Seattle Office of Arts and Culture. Her fiction and essays have been published in *The Rumpus, Salon, Seattle Review of Books,* and *Vol. 1 Brooklyn,* among others. A Made at Hugo House fellow, Mooney is based in Seattle.

Juleen Eun Sun Johnson *(Beat or Beet?)* was born in Seoul, South Korea. She was adopted and taken to Valdez, Alaska. Johnson earned an MFA in Visual Studies from PNCA, and is currently an MFA candidate in Poetry at the University of Massachusetts Amherst. Johnson will be attending Oxford University this summer. Her work has been published in *Cirque: A Literary Journal,* N*ervous Breakdown, The Rio Grande Review, The Dunes Review, The Indianapolis Review, The Cortland Review,* and other journals and anthologies. Johnson is a MacDowell Colony Fellow and an Isabella Gardner Fellow. Having previously lived in Portland, she currently writes and creates art in Massachusetts.

Sarah María Medina *(Rhapsody No. X)* is a poet and a fiction/creative non-fiction writer from the American Northwest. Her writing has been published in *Prelude, Black Warrior Review, Poetry NW, Raspa Literary*

Journal, and elsewhere. Her work is also found in *Nepantla: An Anthology Dedicated to Queer Poets of Color* (Nightboat Books, 2018), and *Bettering American Poetry Vol. 2*. She is the recipient of an ARTIST UP Grant LAB, a Jack Straw Writer fellowship, a Caldera AIR 2018, and the Black Warrior Review poetry prize.

Natalie Villacorta *(Revelations)* is a half Filipino writer from McLean, Virginia. After studying biology and English at Brown University, she worked as a reporter for *Politico*. She left journalism to pursue her MFA in creative nonfiction at Oregon State University, graduating in June 2018. She is now a PhD student in Creative Writing at the University of Cincinnati, where she is an Albert C. Yates Fellow. Her creative writing has appeared in *DIAGRAM* and *The Offing*.

Brandon Jordan Brown (*O Tired Love   it's easy to see the wire that connects*) is a 2014 PEN America Emerging Voices Fellow, winner of the 2016 Orison Anthology Poetry Prize, a scholarship recipient from *The Sun*, and a former PEN in the Community poetry instructor. His work has appeared or is forthcoming in *RHINO Poetry*, *Sycamore Review*, *Yemassee*, *The Journal*, *Forklift, Ohio* and elsewhere. Born in Birmingham, Alabama, he now lives in Portland, Oregon.

Megan Snyder-Camp *(Epimetheus in the Shower)* is the author of three collections of poetry: *The Forest of Sure Things* (Tupelo Press, 2010), *Wintering* (Tupelo Press, 2016), and *The Gunnywolf* (Bear Star Press, 2016). Her poems have appeared in *Antioch Review*, *Sonora Review*, *ZYZZYVA*, and elsewhere. She is the recipient of an Individual Artist grant from 4Culture as well as residencies and scholarships at Djerassi, Bread Loaf, and the Espy Foundation. She lives in Seattle.

Maya Jewell Zeller *(Office Girl & University Hero, Chapter One:* Change*)* is the author of the interdisciplinary collaboration (with visual artist Carrie

DeBacker) *Alchemy For Cells & Other Beasts* (Entre Rios Books, 2017), the chapbook *Yesterday, the Bees* (Floating Bridge Press, 2015), and the poetry collection *Rust Fish* (Lost Horse Press, 2011). Her prose also appears widely, and you can find out what else Office Woman and University Hero are up to in *Booth: A Journal*, and soon over at *Menacing Hedge*. Maya teaches for Central Washington University and edits poetry for Scablands Books.

Savannah Slone *(this is the beneath)* is a queer writer who is completing her MFA in the Pacific Northwest. Her poetry and short fiction has appeared in or will soon appear in *Heavy Feather Review, Ghost City Press, decomP magazinE, Maudlin House, FIVE:2:ONE, Pidgeonholes, TERSE Journal, Glass*, and elsewhere. Her debut poetry chapbook, "Hearing the Underwater," is forthcoming from Finishing Line Press.

Shankar Narayan *(Instruction Manual for Child)* received a 4Culture grant for Claiming Space, a project to lift the voices of writers of color, and his chapbook, *Postcards From the New World*, won the Paper Nautilus Debut Series prize. He is the winner of the 2017 Flyway Sweet Corn Poetry Prize, and has been a fellow at Kundiman and at Hugo House.

Stephanie Wong Ken *(Vacation)* received her MFA from Portland State University. Her writing has appeared in *Joyland, Catapult*, and *Pithead Chapel*, among others. She is currently based in Alberta, Canada.

Chelsea Dingman *(Alchemy)* is the author of the chapbook, *What Bodies Have I Moved* (Madhouse Press, 2018); her first book, *Thaw*, was chosen by Allison Joseph to win the National Poetry Series (University of Georgia Press, 2017). She has won *The Southeast Review*'s Gearhart Poetry Prize, *Sycamore Review*'s Wabash Prize, *Water-stone Review*'s Jane Kenyon Poetry Prize, and the South Atlantic Modern Language Association's Creative Writing Award for Poetry. Her work is forthcoming in *Poetry Northwest, Redivider*, and *The Southern Review*, among others.

Matt Greene *(Something Must be Done!)* holds an MFA from Eastern Washington University. Greene's writing has appeared in or is forthcoming from the *Pacific Northwest Inlander, Santa Monica Review,* and *Spillway.*

Kamari Bright *(The Garden)* is an emerging creative who has had poetry featured in *NILVX: A Book of Magic, 2018 Jack Straw Writers Anthology,* and Bellwether Arts Week. Her video poems have screened at Tacoma Film Festival, Cadence Video Poetry Festival, and Airstream Poetry Festival, and her work will be featured in the 2019 Festival International du Film Pan-Africain de Cannes.

J. C. Sibara *(Three Bullets)* was born and raised in Portland, Oregon, and is now an assistant professor of literature at Colby College in Maine.

Dawn Pichón Barron *(Quantifiable)* is a writer and educator. She earned her MFA at Queens University of Charlotte, NC and is currently working on her Ph.D. in Indigenous Development & Advancement. She is the Director of the Native Pathways Program and member of the Faculty at The Evergreen State College. Her work has appeared in *Yellow Medicine Review, Pittsburgh Poetry Review, Of A Monstrous Child* (Lost Horse Press, 2011), *WA 129* (Sage Press, 2017), and her chapbook, *ESCAPE GIRL BLUES* (Finishing Line Press, 2018). She lives in the Pacific Northwest.

Ian Denning *(Lucy's Midnight Story)* has been published in *The Guardian, Ploughshares, New Ohio Review,* Tin House's *Open Bar,* and elsewhere. A fiction editor for *Pacifica Literary Review,* he has previously edited for *The Bellingham Review, Barnstorm,* and elsewhere. He co-curated *Continue? The Boss Fight Books Anthology,* and tends bar at Hugo House in Seattle.

Michelle Peñaloza *(When Will We Ache Less)* is author of two chapbooks, *Last Night I Dreamt of Volcanoes* (Organic Weapon Arts, 2015) and *landscape/heartbreak* (Two Sylvias, 2015). Her full-length collection, *Former*

Possessions of the Spanish Empire (Inlandia Institute, 2019), recently won the 2018 Hillary Gravendyk National Poetry Prize. Winner of the 2019 Scotti Merrill Emerging Writer Award for Poetry, Michelle is the recipient of scholarships from Caldera, VONA/Voices, and the Bread Loaf Writers' Conference, along with fellowships from Kundiman and Hugo House.

Quenton Baker *(Transient)* is a poet, educator, and Cave Canem fellow. His work has appeared in the anthologies *Measure for Measure: An Anthology of Poetic Meters* and *It Was Written: Poetry Inspired by Hip-Hop*. A 2017 Jack Straw Fellow and a former Made at Hugo House fellow, as well as the recipient of the 2016 James W. Ray Venture Project Award and the 2018 Arts Innovator Award from Artist Trust, Baker is the author of *This Glittering Republic* (Willow Books, 2016). He has an MFA in Poetry from the University of Southern Maine.

Moss was founded by **Connor Guy**, a book editor based in New York, and **Alex Davis-Lawrence**, a filmmaker and creative producer based in Los Angeles. Both were born and raised in Seattle. Moss is:

Editors
Connor Guy
Alex Davis-Lawrence

Contributing Editors
Sharma Shields
Michael Chin
M. Allen Cunningham
Elisabeth Sherman
Diana Xin
Steven L. Moore

Director of Outreach
Amy Wilson

Poetry Editors
Ashley Toliver
Dujie Tahat

Readers
Sasheem Silkiss-Hero
Paisley Green
Elissa Favero
Jenny Liou

Acknowledgments.

Moss is proud to be a subscriber-supported journal. We owe an ongoing debt of gratitude to all our readers, writers, friends, and subscribers—particularly our Patrons, whose exceptional annual support makes our work possible:

Diann Barry and Mark Guy
Max Boyd
Alba Conte
Diane Davis
Ilana Davis-Lawrence
Ronnie-Gail Emden
Naomi Gibbs
Joe Grube
Paul Lawrence and Cynthia Jones
Tod Marshall
Colleen McMonagle and Anthony Peters
Delaney Nye
Valarie Smith
Kaye and Robert Woods

Interested in subscribing?

Visit patreon.com/mosslit to support Northwest writing and get the annual print edition delivered to your door.